Date Due

MAR 2 1			
FEB 2 4 1992			
		WITHDRAWN	

PRINTED IN U. S. A.

the BEDOUINS

the BEDOUINS

olga hoyt

ILLUSTRATED WITH PHOTOGRAPHS

lothrop, lee & shepard co., new york

I wish to thank all those who have given assistance in the preparation of the manuscript for *The Bedouins*. My very special thanks go to Professor H. Bayly Winder, Chairman of the Department of Near Eastern Languages and Literatures of New York University, who most kindly read the manuscript and offered suggestions and corrections. Without his help the book could not be totally accurate, as I now hope it truly is.

Olga Hoyt

Bomoseen, Vermont
August, 1968

To Dinny

6289

MAP BY GIULIO MAESTRO

contents

TURKEY

ARMENIA

CYPRUS

MEDITERRANEAN
SEA

SYRIA

IRAQ

Beirut

LEBANON

Damascus

Baghdad

Syrian Desert

ISRAEL

Alexandria

Port
Said

Jerusalem

Suez

JORDAN

SINAI
PENIN-
SULA

Kuwait

UNITED ARAB
REPUBLIC
(Egypt)

SAUDI

Medina

RED

ARABIA

SEA

Mecca

YEMEN

EAST
AD

SOUTH ARABIA

Aden GULF OF
ADEN

Maestro

CASPIAN SEA

Tehran

IRAN
(Persia)

AFGHANISTAN

WEST
PAKISTAN

PERSIAN
GULF

TRUCIAL STATES

GULF OF OMAN

MUSCAT
&
OMAN

Muscat

ARABIAN

SEA

The Middle East

one

WHO ARE THE BEDOUINS?

As far as the eye can see across miles of desert, the dry sandy plain is covered with scores of black tents and a hundred times that many fawn-colored camels. At the center, in the middle of a patch of purple flowers, sits the sheikh's big black tent, set on nine poles. The tent is made of coarse cloth woven of goat's hair, and it covers a hundred square yards. Several mares and colts graze nearby in the lush vegetation. Inside, a hundred people can take shelter from the burning sun, as they sit on handsome carpets and lean against camel saddles. In the center of the tent by the hearth are the tall coffeepots and a long coffee ladle, a sign that guests are always welcome here in this rich Bedouin camp.

Far away on the desert is another Bedouin camp. Here a handful of barefoot, ragged, unkempt children play near a battered little tent settlement. A few scrawny horses graze among the scattered tents. The sheikh, a little old man in rags, beckons his guests into a dirty tent no larger than any other. A young bull is tied in one corner inside and a rough-

Black Bedouin tents in Saudi Arabia.

Arabian American Oil Company.

looking mare in another. There are scraps of carpet and ragged saddles. This sheikh is the leader of a poor tribe that counts as its sole riches a few goats and sheep. But the same coffeepots and ladle are here, too, by the fire. Bedouin hospitality is the same for the rich or poor.

The year could be 1966 or 1866, or even 1066, for the true wanderers of the desert have been living thus since before the time of Christ.

Bedouin is the transliteration of the Arabic word *badawy*, which means "inhabitant of the desert." These nomadic peoples have been coursing the deserts in and around the Arabian Peninsula for thousands of years. From the Mediterranean and the Red Sea to the Persian Gulf in what is now Egypt, in other areas of North Africa, Saudi Arabia, Yemen, Oman, Jordan, Syria, Lebanon and Iraq, the Bedouins have roamed the lands, following the rainfall, searching for the wells of brackish water that lie buried in the sand, or seeking the green grass in the valley.

Often the Bedouin is referred to as "the original Arab." It is only in recent times that the term *Arab* has included all those who speak the Arabic language. In the early days *Arab* meant the Bedouin, the wanderer who lived in the desert—he was in a group apart from the village dwellers and the farmers. The origin of the word *Arab* itself is obscure; however, it is generally regarded as a derivation from an ancient word, *abar*, or "pass," implying nomadism.

Writings from the pre-Christian period which have been deciphered only in the last few centuries show that many different peoples inhabited northern Africa, the Arabian Peninsula, and the lands nearby, where today the Bedouins are to be found. It was established that their common an-

Camels resting in front of a Bedouin camp.

Arabian American Oil Company.

cestors were the Semites, of whom the Arabs were one group. The earliest known mass settlement of Arabs took place in Yemen, in the southwestern part of the peninsula. Then, as that population grew, the first Arab migration set out around 3500 B.C., up along the west coast of Arabia, through Sinai into Egypt. They mixed with the peoples there. Another group moved up the eastern portion of the peninsula and settled in the Tigris-Euphrates valley. One culture after another—among them the Babylonians, Assyrians, Chaldeans, and Phoenicians—struggled for control of the various areas as groups moved in, conquered, and ruled for a time until they, too, were replaced by more ag-

gressive peoples. Cities arose, such as Damascus, which is considered the oldest surviving city in the modern world; trade flourished, as goods were carried by camels up the Red Sea coast through Mecca to Egypt and the Mediterranean.

Yet the vast desert wastes of Arabia—largely because of their very forbidding nature—were left to the Bedouins. So changes of rulers and cultures swirled around the desert dwellers, leaving them basically untouched. The Bedouin of 1500 years ago lived, ate, slept, journeyed, and traded much as the Bedouin does today. This is significant, because through the years the desert dwellers had opportuni-

13

Arab tribes on the move. From an 1885 drawing.

ties to leave the wasteland forever, and take up the cloak of more civilized society. Some Bedouins, of course, did so, and became village people, but the vast majority, after contact with more sophisticated living, lapsed back into the peacefulness of their nomadic lives.

The rise of Christianity led to one of the first assaults upon the Bedouin's way of life. Having successfully converted large numbers of pagan Arabs in Northern Arabia, the Christians sought to impose their religion and rule upon the Bedouins of southern and central Arabia. There most of the Bedouins worshipped the moon. Soon the Jews became rivals with the Christians in trying to rid the Bedouins of their moon worship. However, it was not until the time of Mohammed that the Bedouins accepted a formalized nonpagan religion.

An old picture of a typical Bedouin.

New York Public Library.

Mohammed was born in Mecca in 571 A.D. and was raised on the desert by a Bedouin shepherd's wife. When he was about forty years old he received a "call;" he heard the voice of an angel tell him he was the Prophet of Allah. There was but one God, and that God was Allah. Thus Mohammed founded the religion of Islam—the "surrender" to the will of God—which was to become a world religion. The Bedouin tribes had been living for centuries according to the traditions of their ancestors. Now, conditioned by Christian and Jewish influences, they accepted Islam and were largely responsible for its spread.

To understand this acceptance, one must understand the nature of the Bedouin. The Bedouins lived in tribes, and all members of a tribe had in principle a blood relationship with one another. Their view of the world centered on what was called *Muruwwa. Muruwwa* was all the glory the Bedouin believed he had inherited from his noble ancestors. This glory imposed obligations and duties, all revolving around family ties. The motto was, "all for one and one for all." *Asabiyya*—tribal solidarity—was valued above all else. The desert Arab gave his life and loyalty to his tribe. The tribes lived on harsh land, where the sun was hot and the winds cruel. They depended for their livelihood on two things: their sheep or camels, and the raids they launched against neighboring settlements, or against the many caravans that wound their slow way across the deserts.

Mohammed at first had only a few converts to his new religion; then those followers invited Mohammed to make his home with them in the ancient city of Yathrib, several hundred miles north of Mecca. Thus came about the flight north—called the *Hijrah,* from which the Moslem Era was later designated as beginning. (As *Islam* meant submission, *Moslem* was from the word for one who submits.) Mohammed settled in Yathrib, which he renamed Medina, short for *Madinat al-Nabi,* the City of the Prophet. Mohammed, now head of a community, turned from the use of persuasion to the use of the sword. He said that he had been sent to lead the faithful to the destruction of all who refused obedience to the law of Islam. Mohammed became not only a religious leader, but also a political ruler. His goal was the imposition of Islam on all his pagan countrymen. He conceived a new ruling unit, the *Umma,* which was like a new tribe with Mohammed as its leader and Islam as its ideology. To spread its power and increase its wealth the *Umma* raided caravans and did battle with neighboring rulers. And in all this, the Bedouin tribes were most important. The Bedouins accepted Islam as a system for procuring the good things of life for themselves. They were used to raiding to increase their wealth. In their religious zeal and the desire for booty, the Bedouin tribes joined Mohammed's other followers in their conquests.

Medina was made secure. Then military thrusts went out in all directions. There were many raids. Mecca was taken. Just as Islam seemed to be greatly advancing in converts and tribute, Mohammed fell ill and died in 632. Mohammed had united the Arabs under the banner of one God; were they now to fail in their mission? Perhaps they might have, but they did not, because of the courage and devotion of Mohammed's faithful disciples. Under the leadership of these men, the Bedouin tribes surged into Syria and seized Damascus. Jerusalem surrendered. The Arabs pressed north along the Tigris River. The whole of Iraq fell to them. After a decade of trying, they conquered all of Persia. Then Egypt was moved upon by the southern Arabian Bedouin tribes.

Through all this military adventure the Bedouins used the desert for supplies and communications. They used the desert as a retreat when defeated. They were desert-born

A man of the desert. From *The Seven Pillars of Wisdom* by T. E. Lawrence, 1926, 1935, by Doubleday and Co., Inc.

and desert-bred, and so when they settled in conquered territory they set up their encampments at the borders of the desert. And here, though they were to be united as brothers under the belief in God, they still were quartered out by the old tribal allegiances.

Damascus became the center of what was now, through conquests, a full-fledged Arab kingdom. The Arabs went into North Africa and imposed Islam on the Berber tribes, and together the two groups mounted a campaign against Spain. But when, in the eighth century, they attempted to invade France, they were defeated and the Arab-Berber thrust was stopped. Thus ended the Arab movement into Western Europe.

In a space of eighty years after Mohammed's death the Arab Moslems conquered an area far larger than the Romans had been able to conquer in eight hundred years, but now came changes for the Bedouins. As the Arab Moslems took over more and more peoples, the Bedouins became a minority. They began vanishing from the government that they had helped establish. Now they started to abandon their great "encampment cities." They went back to their deserts and their nomadic way of living, or they began settling on farms, where they soon became peasants. As the years passed the Persians seized power over the Arabs, and then the Turks conquered. The Bedouins faded into the desert wilderness.

They were called upon by the Allies for military service in World War I, when the Arabs revolted against the Turks. Bedouin tribes helped the British take over territory held by the German and Turkish troops, enabling the British to enter Jerusalem. The British regained Damascus and held much other territory at the War's end.

Now the glory that once was the Islamic empire is gone. The Moslem world is split into many states. The nomads who helped create that empire now scarcely play a role in these countries. Cultures have come and gone through the centuries, yet until recent years the Bedouins have been largely untouched by the march of civilization. Whether they will be "nationalized" by various governments remains to be seen. In the changing modern world the Bedouins are becoming more and more isolated as economic growth and security come to the peoples around them.

the BeÐouin tribes

The Bedouins have always preserved their ancient customs and age-old traditions. Today they camp not far from ruined palaces and ancient fortifications that belonged to early Arab princes more than two thousand years ago. They wander past crumbling temples and caravan cities, traces left from the Greek, Roman, and Byzantine conquests.

For over three thousand years the Syrian Desert has linked the eastern shores of the Mediterranean Sea with what was once Mesopotamia (now called Iraq). The vast desert of Arabia lies between two of the best trade routes, the Red Sea and the Persian Gulf. In all the desert areas the Bedouins lived, moving across the shifting sands. They are self-contained even yet, still largely cut off from the rest of the world.

Whether they are in Syria, Iraq, or Saudi Arabia, the Bedouins live a primitive existence, dependent on their animals. They breed, raise, and sell camels, and live from the products of sheep and goats. Not all Bedouin tribes

The Bedouins are dependent upon their animals.
Arabian American Oil Company.

own camels; some have only sheep and goats. Bedouins are constantly searching for water and pasturage for their animals, wandering with the change of seasons—only a few miles when they are lucky or, if they are unlucky, making a week's march.

Each Bedouin is a part of his community, the general tribe, which directly governs all his actions. The tribe can be powerful, such as the Ruala in northern Arabia, or it can be a small tribe that has only fifty tents. The tribes, even those which claim common ancestors, have changed through the centuries because of war or because strong groups have broken away and formed new tribes. Thus many of the great bands of thousands of years ago have vanished, and new groups have been formed. Tribal names change, too, and often old tribal names disappear. This is especially true if they are unflattering, such as *Beni Kelb,*

21

"Children of the Dog." That tribe changed its name half a century ago. The members of each tribe have always called themselves the children—*beni* in Arabic—of their tribe. Thus there were the *Beni Ghassan* of ancient Jordan, who today are the *Beni Sakhr* of Jordan.

Every tribe of Bedouins has its leader, or sheikh. He represents the tribe in transactions with other tribes or with the outside world. Each tribe has subsections, or clans, which are close associations of families. But no matter how many divisions and subdivisions there are in a clan, all its members consider themselves to be of one blood, owing allegiance to the parent tribe. Because there is much inter-marriage within the clan, the members often resemble one another strikingly.

Each clan has its petty sheikh, and from among the petty sheikhs is chosen the sheikh proper. He is the "father of his people," a "first among equals." He is powerful, but only in conjunction with his lesser sheikhs. These men form the council, and must be consulted in matters of peace and war, or even on the choice of a new site for encampment. Once a tribal council has given its approval, the sheikh assumes full power of command to carry out the plan, and his orders are to be obeyed.

Some sheikhs are wealthy. They have the tribal lands, and they acquire wealth through commissions they receive for contracts for camel hire, through breeding their herds, and sometimes by raids. The raid in past years was a na-tional institution, and was considered both a necessary and a manly occupation for all Bedouins. However, in modern times, governments with armored cars and air-craft are alert to prevent raiding.

The Bedouin Tribes

The office of sheikh usually passes from father to son, but merit is of prime importance. Perhaps the eldest son inherits the position, but before doing so, he must prove that he has the necessary courage, powers of leadership, and good luck. Luck (*hadh*) is an important attribute for a tribal sheikh.

The clans are really the permanent elements of the Bedouin community, while the tribe is the general group. Since the tribe with its many clans is very large, it is generally impossible for a whole tribe to move together from water source to water source. Thus the clans wander by themselves, in their own cycles, within the land, called *dirah,* customarily used by the tribe itself. Each tribesman knows just where these boundaries lie on the seemingly boundless desert, even though the *dirah* may change from time to time.

As the clan is responsible to the tribe, Bedouins are responsible directly to the clan, and in turn the clan is responsible for each of its members. Blood money, for the murder of a clan member, is payable to all members in varying degrees, according to the closeness of their re-

A camp in the desert.   *Arabian American Oil Company.*

lationship to the victim. By the same token, all, including five generations of a family, must contribute toward the payment of the blood money if the slayer is a member of the clan.

Although blood is the basic consideration in the clan, honorary membership may be obtained by an outsider. This, however, may be just a temporary membership. A guest must be protected by his host so long as the food they have eaten together remains in his belly. Nothing more than the act of eating bread and salt together is necessary to make people become wayfellows, who are bound to defend each other on a march through certain territory.

One Englishman, traveling in Egypt during the first quarter of the nineteenth century, expressed his concern about the dangers of an expedition, whereupon the eldest of the Arab party immediately drew his sword, placed some salt on the blade, and then put a portion of it into his mouth. He instructed the Englishman to do the same. "Now, cousin," the Bedouin said, "your life is as sacred to me as my own." (What he actually said was, "Son of my uncle, your head is upon my shoulders.") The Arab feels that this "good brothership" confers real kinship on the guest. Once a passing stranger merely tied his rope to a tribesman's well rope. He was regarded as a guest, and when he was later killed by another tribe, blood money was demanded and obtained.

A clan may also be increased when a family feels itself mistreated by its own sheikh, and takes refuge with the sheikh of another clan by pitching its tent beside his. The protector is bound to be responsible for the family members, and in a few generations they consider that they actually belong to the new clan and tribe. If the clan that has sheltered a Bedouin is raided by the clan of his origin, he is expected to protect or recover the goods of the two tents on either side of his in his new clan.

Within the clan structure, the next unit is the family. An old sheikh once said that the wealth of the Arabs is in their children. That is why most sheikhs are ambitious to have immense families, and why some sheikhs have many wives. Only a lack of wealth will restrict a sheikh to one wife. Though the average Bedouin theoretically may have more than one wife, he generally has only one at a time.

In the family, a father is strict. He does not allow a boy to sit down or to eat in his presence, and the sons are taught to be independent at an early age. All Bedouin children are noted for their self-reliance. The Bedouin woman, even after she is married, belongs to her father's family, and that family is always responsible for her. Once when two women were battling beside a well, the husband of the losing lady was observed merely standing by, without attempting to aid his wife. On being urged to help, he replied, "Certainly not, it would mix up the settlement. Let her brothers and father come to the rescue. It is their business."

The Bedouin men have no responsibility except to take care of the camel herds and protect the tribe. Most of them are content to sleep, talk, smoke, and drink coffee to pass the day. The women set up the tents, bring the water, do the cooking, baking, and weaving, and tend the children. Young boys and girls are out from dawn until dusk on the hillsides, herding the sheep and the goats, drinking the

25

The men often have coffee during the day.

Arabian American Oil Company.

milk of their charges when hungry. Boys are set free from this task when they are seven or eight years of age, the girls when they are twice as old and considered marriageable.

Each Bedouin family pitches its tent in an assigned location near others at the encampment. When the camping site has been selected by the sheikh, after discussion with his council, the sheikh strikes down the shaft of his tall horseman's lance, which is twice or three times as long as his horse. This action indicates his authority and the fellowship of the clan. His tent is then raised, and if it does not include seating places for the council (*mejlis*), a separate tent is erected close by. The sheikh's tent is placed in a prominent or central position. The other tents are pitched around in a recognized plan, generally with the camp forming a rectangle. The encampment is never far from water for the Bedouins and their animals, and is chosen for the availability of good pasturage. Some camps are close to deep *wadis* (low valley ground), which are well watered and rich in grass; some are near a mound in the middle of a plain; some are at the bottom of gently

An encampment is never far from water.
Arabian American Oil Company.

sloping hills, and some are in the hollows of high land. The camps, however, are always within the boundaries of the tribal properties, lest there be war.

The tent (*beit sha'r,* or "house of hair") is a long rectangular structure, composed of strips of strong coarse cloth woven from black goat's hair, thrown over a framework of poles. Each cloth strip is about three-quarters of a yard in width and runs the full length of the tent. A rich sheikh might need strips ten yards long, while a poor Bedouin would need only half that amount. Six or eight of these strips are stitched together forming a rectangular covering, which is raised on tent poles. The sides are stretched taut by means of tent ropes. The walls are made of one or two wool strips and a piece of sackcloth, which trails on the ground. One side of the tent is open along the entire length, except for the part occupied by the women and little children, and that is partially closed. The tent cloth at the back generally faces the prevailing northwest wind and can be easily moved, according to the wind and sun, so that the back can become the front. The good wife knows when this should be done, and will unpin and move the cloth.

The tallest part of the tent is high enough for the tallest man to stand erect. The tent is divided into two parts by a hanging curtain, so that the men can be separated from the women. The tent of a chief might be divided into two or three parts—one part for feasts and entertainment for tribesmen and guests (and for council meetings), one for the women and children, and a third for storage of household goods and baggage.

The pitching of the tent is always the woman's job,

The Bedouin Tribes

whether the family is rich enough to afford slaves or not. (Generally only sheikhs own slaves.) The father may direct the operation, but the wife and children raise the structure in place, each knowing his own job and the sequence of the work. Daughters of the house, for example, usually hammer the pegs which hold the ropes. For this they might use stone hammers.

After the tent has been pitched, carpets are unrolled in the men's portion; saddlebags made of wool, brightly colored and ornamented with tassels, are put in place for reclining. A fireplace to make coffee is dug in the center of the floor by scraping out a circular hole. Coffeepots and cups, roaster and stirrer, the mortar and pestle for grinding the beans, and perhaps an incense burner are among the other items on the men's side of the tent. The

Coffee-making equipment is kept on the men's side of the tent.
Arabian American Oil Company.

women's portion of the tent contains their quarters and the cooking area. There are sacks made of tent cloth for storing the household goods: [corn, rice, sugar, coffee,] and salt, and calico, wool, and yarn to be made into clothing for the family. There are also cooking utensils such as copper cooking pans or stone pots, griddles, sieves, a mortar for pounding corn, and a mill for grinding it. Quilts are rolled up and placed on top of the stores, and there is usually a spindle in evidence.

Outside, but close to the women's quarters, lie the filled waterskins, which are placed on a thick layer of brush so that they will stay cool. Water buckets and a tripod with a goatskin hanging below it stand ready to make yogurt, which the Arabs call *leben*.

The most prized possession of the Bedouin housewife is the private box in which she stores her few ornaments. Perhaps she owns a gold or silver nose ring, or a few bracelets and bangles, inherited from her family. She brings these out for show from time to time. These and a few objects belonging to her husband are in her keeping, and are placed under lock and key. If her husband is rich the Bedouin wife will have a larger box, in which most of the sheikh's valuables are placed, but he will be sure that the key will hang on his belt rather than on the woman's veil.

Once the tent is erected, and the household goods are organized in a new camp, the Bedouins are ready to begin daily life, hoping for good water and healthy pasturage for their chief assets—their animals. Soon the heavy smell of coffee and the sour smell of *leben* are in the air. Life begins anew.

daily life in a typical bedouin camp

"Allah-U-Akbar," the words ring out. It is the call to morning prayer, the first of five prayers during the day. It is still dark, for it is only four A.M., yet the time has come, just before dawn, when a single hair held before the eyes can be seen—the time for the first prayer. One of the men has called the Bedouins to worship, and now the others hasten to become clean before praying. If no water is at hand, Allah's followers wash with sand. Then they face Mecca and pray. The women of the household remain in their black tents praying alone.

Then the camp begins to become lively. The animals awaken, these beasts who are the cherished possession and livelihood of the nomads. The sheep and the camels have slept the night in a semicircle in front of the camp, the closeness and the warmth of their bodies and the nearness of the tent protecting them from the cold winds. Now the shepherds—servants or unmarried young men—call their flocks of sheep together or the camel men talk to their camels. Generally a Bedouin tribe will have mainly camels, along with a few sheep, which have a difficult time grazing on the desert, and some goats. If a tribe is of small means they will have only sheep. During the night each of the lambs has been tied up by a woolen loop to a central rope in the tent. The lambs all begin to bleat at once. Each lamb is suckled by its mother, then it is tied up again. After this breakfast, the lambs will get nothing until night-fall.

The wife of the household, having seen that coffee is being prepared, has gone to make the *leben,* the curdled milk of sheep and goats. *Rug-rug-rug-rug* sounds the goat-skin of milk as it is rocked. *Rug-rug-rug.* For two hours the woman will rock the goatskin as it hangs down on the wooden tripod. Sometimes she sings as she makes the butter and the *leben* that is the life beverage of the Bedouins.

By now dawn is beginning to break, and the young men in charge of the animals begin the daily counting of the sheep. If there are fewer sheep this morning than were bedded down last night, all know that a wolf has stolen into camp and carried off the sheep. A sheep is so fright-ened when it is seized by a wolf that it cannot cry out; only goats will cry when attacked. When the counting is over, the shepherd boy is given some coffee and some dates. He eats a few of his dates and puts the rest in a little leather bag. They will be his day's food. He rounds up his charges and takes them three or four miles out into the desert to graze. His will not be a hard day, though it will be a long one.

When the shepherd has found a good grazing spot, he will most likely plant his staff nearby in the sand and

Daily Life in a Typical Bedouin Camp

place his *'Abba*, his cloak, on his stick. This *'Abba* is much like a scarecrow. The sheep and lambs think it is the shepherd, standing near them and watching, so they will not wander. The shepherd is free to find a comfortable spot in the sand and sleep most of the day away.

By this time the women and children at the camp have milked the young camels, and the herdsman has given the older camels a few mouthsful of dates to encourage them to be up and away for their grazing. He leads the animals off, riding on the hindquarters of a camel, with the others following behind in single file. The camel herder's is a harder task than that of the shepherd, for

A young camel has his breakfast.

Arabian American Oil Company.

Boys lead their herd over the plain in search of grass.
Arabian American Oil Company.

the camel herd must go perhaps eight miles through the desert sands, and the herder must watch the camels closely with his rifle ready, to see that no harm—from man or beast—will befall them.

The young girls of the household have their jobs to perform in the morning, too. Sometimes the very young may be sent out to herd the sheep and goats from dawn to dusk on the hillsides. The lucky young daughters are allowed to go with their older sisters when they are sent out to collect brushwood. The little ones skip along looking for flowers or truffles. The older girls are seeking *'Arfaj*, a bush with a tough root, which is used for the tent fires and for making a pile outside the tent upon which to rest the waterskins. They go barefoot, with their skirts hitched up at the waist. The long sleeves of their dresses, which are slit under the arms, the girls tie behind their necks to free their arms. They carry small axes and goat's-hair rope. The axes are needed to cut the tough roots of the 'Arfaj; the rope is to tie up the firewood. After a two- to three-mile walk, which takes about two hours, the girls return to the tent site, each bearing an enormous load of 'Arfaj bushes on her head.

While the children are gone, the woman of the household continues her daily chores. She is a highly honored person. She is the Umm al-'Ayyal—the mother of the family —and she is responsible, too, for the honor and good name of her husband within the tribe. She not only is in charge of his tent, but she cooks, bakes, weaves, makes her own clothes, supervises the children, makes leben, and though she does not mix socially with male strangers, she prepares choice and tasty dishes for these guests she never sees, so that the hospitality of the tent is held in esteem.

There is much to do. The woman of the household, perhaps with the help of her sister or mother, suns the family bedding and puts it away. She cleans the pots and pans and other kitchen equipment from the previous night's dinner. She tidies up the tent, and sends the family's spare shepherd out to fetch water from the wells they last visited. This shepherd may have to make a long journey, perhaps ten miles back. He will take a few male camels and load them with two camel waterskins or four goatskins. These filled will be enough for the tent and perhaps for a neighbor. Water is a constant problem in the desert. If there is only a scanty amount for the tent, the young girls may be sent out to collect water from a nearby *thamila*. A *thamila* is a small supply of water which lies under the surface of a dry, sandy watercourse. The water does not sink deep or disappear completely because it lies on rock or clay beneath the surface.

The girls go out with goatskins. They scratch away the sand until they have dug down about two or three feet. There they find brown, muddy water. They ladle it into the skins with a small cup of tamarisk wood. The water will at first be yellowish, but when the silt settles it will be suitable for drinking. Then it is back to camp, where the waterskins are laid on a bed of 'Arfaj bushes just outside the women's quarters, so that they will stay cool.

If the nomad family is fairly well-to-do, there will be lunch. This may consist of cooked rice, with butter made from sheep's milk. Many times, however, the meal will be only a little milk, and whatever scraps are left from the previous day. Some Bedouins feel lucky if they have a piece of dry bread soaked in water.

After the noon hour the housewife will clean any dirty dishes, then start weaving cloth to be used for the repair of the tent. Every humble tribal woman makes and renews the worn parts of her tent; only those with means go into the towns to buy. The best tent material is made of goat's hair alone. It is thick, and jet black.

The tent work done, she might work on a *Qata*, a gaily decorated tent curtain made of four strips sewn together, which she will sell when the tribe next visits a town on one of its migrations.

An hour or so before sunset the woman will order the household to prepare and fill the large leather drinking

A Bedouin woman spins wool, which may be used to repair the tent.   *Arabian American Oil Company.*

trough, from which the sheep and the master's mare will drink when they come home. The sheep will probably not need much, and it is so difficult to water the camels in the camp that the herdsman takes them back to a handy well every fifth day. The mare will drink much. She has probably pastured all day near the camp, tethered by an iron chain which fastens her forefeet one to the other. At night the mare's foot is passed through an iron ring at one end of a long chain, which is then locked up. The other end of the chain is fastened to an iron spike, which the owner drives into the ground at the place in his tent where he will sleep. The mare is his most precious possession, so he takes care not to lose her.

In the late afternoon the housewife has a little time to take a walk or enjoy her children. The children have been playing about the tent. Some of the young boys may have been practicing with their slings, gathering round pebbles and throwing them—with great skill. Woe be to anyone who is hit by a pebble whistling thus through the air, for a stone from an Arab sling can fracture the thickest skull.

As the sun is beginning to set, the housewife brings in a bundle of dry bushes, which she places by the hearthside in the men's compartment for the evening fire there. Here in the master's room a shallow circular hole has been dug in the center of the floor for the fire. There are well-worn carpets. The master's camel saddle, covered with white or black sheepskin, is there. When guests are present, pillows will be placed on both sides of the saddle and also behind it for the guests to rest on.

The head of the household has spent most of the day in this compartment, sleeping or dozing or smoking a pipe.

During the day the men may discuss future pasturage for their
animals. *Arabian American Oil Company.*

His responsibilities are only to the tribe's camels, and to
the sheikh, for the protection of the tribe. Some days there
are gatherings in the sheikh's tent, either to receive news
of other tribes or to discuss future pasturage for the animals. Perhaps there might be a camel ride to seek out the
next camping sites, for the Bedouins must move on when
the camels have exhausted the nearby grazing grounds.
But whether a householder has played at *sheidje*, a game
similar to checkers, to pass the time of day, or has been
out engaging himself usefully, he is always ready for the
evening meal—the largest, and for many Bedouins the only,
meal of the day.

If he has been out on his mare, he returns now as the sun is setting. The tent watchdogs, fierce, shaggy dogs, begin to bark. The children rush out of the tent, and the wife orders coffee to be prepared. The wife and daughters take his mare and immediately throw a blanket over her before taking her to water. After watering they shackle her again with the clumsy iron shackles, one ring on each forefoot, connected by a chain, and allow her to pasture as she did earlier in the day. If there is food enough the mare will be given some barley, but if the family is poor the mare will receive nothing more.

It is nearly evening now. The Bedouin retires to his compartment in his tent, while the wife starts the evening meal in the kitchen portion of her compartment.

At sunset the camels come home. This time the herdsman is riding behind them, singing, urging them to hurry up. They are shepherded to the front of the tent, where they lie down in a semicircle, with heads all facing the open side of the tent. An hour after sunset, when often it is quite dark in this land near the equator, the sheep are brought in and led into the semicircle formed by the camels. As the lambs are untied from inside the tent and taken out to their mothers there is much noise and confusion. The young have to be guided to their mothers, who will accept no lamb but their own. Since there is no light except that in the kitchen portion of the tent, there is much fumbling among the animals. But then the lambs are fed, taken back into the tent, and tied up.

The various householders have now dispersed to their own tents to partake of whatever supper the wife has been able to make from their supplies. The sky is dark and the stars shine brightly; there is no more wandering throughout the encampment. The head of the household has retreated to the guest portion of his tent, and now has a small fire going, made with embers of dry camel dung. Every now and then he will put on a small bunch of the *'Arfaj* bush to cause a blaze. Soon his wife brings him his supper: perhaps boiled rice, with a little bread. Then there is *leben* and coffee. The wife, having already eaten a snack with the children, will sit by her husband if he is alone to see that he has all that he needs.

Some Bedouin meals consist of merely a paste made of flour and water, baked in ashes of camel's dung, and mixed with a little butter. Another common dish, also a paste, is made of flour and sour camel's milk and boiled. Or perhaps there will be *burghul,* which is wheat dried in the sun and then soaked or boiled for eating. The *burghul* can be preserved for a year. If there is little to eat in the tent, a paste can be made of bread, butter, and dates. A luxury is the truffle, called *kemmaye* by some. This underground fungus has no root, and lies about four inches beneath the surface. It is often dug up by the children, with short sticks. The truffle is boiled in water or milk till it forms a paste; sometimes it is roasted and eaten with melted butter.

If there is a guest in the tent the fare will be more substantial, for the Bedouins prize their capacity for hospitality above almost all else. For an ordinary guest, bread may be baked and served with *ayesth,* a mixture of flour and sour camel's milk. The bread can be baked in round cakes upon a plate of iron, or by kindling a fire over a circle of a many small stones. When the stones are sufficiently heated, the fire is removed. The paste is then spread over the hot stones, immediately covered with glowing ashes, and left until thoroughly baked. (This latter type of bread is only used at breakfast.)

If the guest is of some consequence there will surely be the bread served with melted butter, and if the guest is of especially high rank a kid or lamb will be killed in his honor. The lamb is often boiled with *burghul* and camel's milk and served in a large wooden dish, around the edge of which the meat is placed. A wooden bowl containing the melted fat of the animal is put in and pressed down in the midst of the *burghul*. Every bit of meat is dipped into the fat before it is swallowed. The Bedouins, who wash their hands before dinner, put their whole right hand into the dish before them, shape the *burghul* into balls, and swallow them. Then they pick out the pieces of meat. When there are guests the men eat alone. If there is a water shortage the men do not wash their hands after dinner, but wipe them on a flap of the tent.

Most often, in the Bedouin encampment, the men eat alone in their black tents. Sometimes for the very poor there is not even a cup of cold sour milk for supper. It is the sheikh, the leader, who receives the camp's guests. If he is a well-to-do sheikh, the meal will be filling. It may be a tender lamb, stuffed with rice and roasted over the ashes of a fire in a pit covered with earth. Then, of course, there is coffee, the thick bitter Arab coffee, both before and after the meal. The host may or may not eat with his guests.

It is about the sheikh's hearth that the men of the camp begin to gather after the evening meal, in expectation of coffee. The camels have just been milked by the men and boys; perhaps the first bowl of frothing milk has been taken to the mare, tethered by the woman's side of the tent. She sups the sweet warm milk through her teeth and snorts and whinnies with pleasure. After she has been fed, the bowl—often the same one used for the mare—is filled and passed among the household.

It is now deep night; the men have gathered in the sheikh's quarters. The old men, and the herdsmen who have been out in the sun all day, are weary and lie now on their elbows about the common fire. The tent householders sit around and talk. The coffee is being made with much ceremony, and the more important the gathering, the more detailed is the ritual of coffee making. It is a solemn and important duty done by the host himself, especially if he is a poor Bedouin who can offer only a poor quality of coffee. (A prominent sheikh might delegate the coffee making to a trusted person or favorite slave.) After the men have brought the dry camel dung, the 'Arfaj brush for making the fire, and the water from the goatskin outside the women's quarters, the host cleans out the fireplace and starts making the fire. He then gets his material and equipment ready—the coffee beans from a bag, and the four coffeepots. Three of the pots are blacked by fire and the fourth, shining and bright, is the one from which the coffee will be poured.

The coffee beans are roasted, cooled, poured into a mortar, and pounded with a pestle. The *ting ting* of the pestle and mortar is one of the pleasantest sounds the Bedouin can hear. The ground coffee is then poured into the *sharbat,* the previous day's coffee to which a little water

The solemn duty of making coffee is performed by the host.
Arabian American Oil Company.

has been added, and which has been boiled. The coffee is stirred, it bubbles, and some cardamom seeds are pounded and added for flavor. The coffee is then poured into the shiny pot, back to a blackened pot, and again to the shiny pot, so that the grounds settle. A piece of hemp is placed in the spout to act as a strainer, and now all is ready! The host pours a small quantity into a cup without handles and drinks it to show that it is not poisoned, and then the guests are served a small amount of coffee in each cup. Anyone may take as many cups as he likes, but good manners usually prevent a guest from taking more than

44

The beans are roasted, then cooled.

Arabian American Oil Company.

The cooled beans are crushed in a mortar.
Arabian American Oil Company.

The brewing pot is placed over the fire.
Arabian American Oil Company.

three cups. When finished, the Bedouin signals that he has
had enough by shaking the empty cup with a half dozen
little shakes of the wrist; then the host takes the cup, fills
it, and gives it to the next person waiting.

Sometimes the men will linger in the sheikh's tent until
midnight, when they retire to their own compartments in
their own tents. But many times they are so weary that
they end their day shortly after supper and camel milking.

47

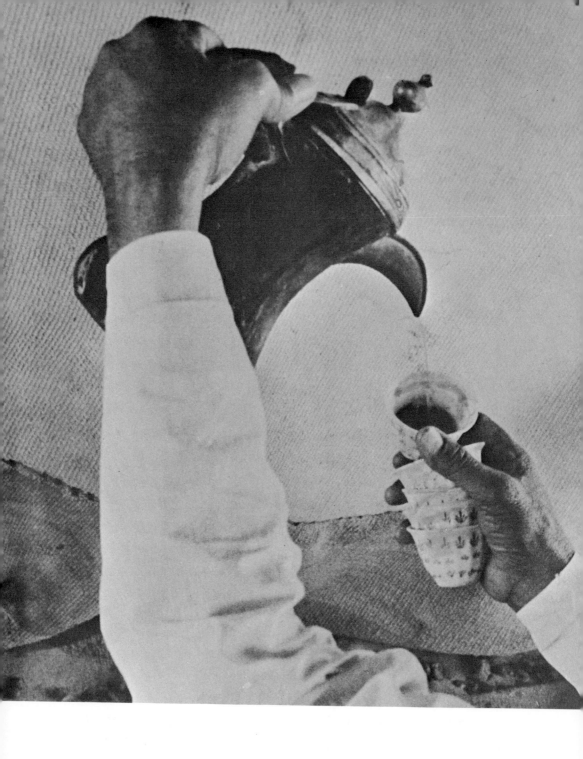

When ready, the coffee is served in thimble-size cups.
Arabian American Oil Company.

Daily Life in a Typical Bedouin Camp

Some nights an energetic householder might go hunting with his falcon. If it is a bright, moonlit evening the boys and girls may troop from their mother's quarters and race over the sand to a rock or hillock, and play at horses. A boy and a girl, hand in hand, skip away ahead of the others, kicking and making believe they are neighing. The other children chase them. The older girls may assemble to watch; they clap their hands and chant, enjoying watching the play. There, too, may come the younger men of the camp to talk and sing with the girls.

The day draws to a close. All has gone well in the camp. Now it is time to sleep, for the daily life will begin again before the sun has risen.

A Bedouin hunter with his prize falcon.
Arabian American Oil Company.

migrations with the seasons

The morrow may well mean a move of the campground. The nomads—the wanderers—must constantly seek new pastureland for their camels and sheep, so from November until May the Bedouins are on the move. The rains have finally come in October, causing the green shoots of plants to spring up in a desert which has been dry all summer. Wetted, the yellow desert begins to take on a pale green coloring.

With the rain clouds gathering in the skies, the Bedouin begins to stir about in his summer camp by the wells, and joyfully looks forward to the almost constant migration that will follow in the coming months. He feels the change in the air. It has become cooler. The sun, wind, and sand-storms of the summer months brought almost unbearable heat. There was little to eat and precious little to drink, but the Bedouins have survived one more year and now the tribe is infected with a perceptible gaiety.

The first move away from the summer encampment and its fixed water point will not be far, for the camels, sheep, and mares must still be watered. In fact, none of the moves—made about every ten days—will be for great distances. The Bedouins will move only when the animals have nibbled to the roots of the grasses in the grazing area. Then it is time to search for a new pasture within the tribal territory.

Each tribe knows the boundaries of its own land, even if they are unmarked. The Bedouins will wander about this territory, seeking out the grass. But if rains have failed in their own territory, then the nomads must seek a pasture

Bedouins on the move. *Arabian American Oil Company.*

in land belonging to a friendly tribe. Few tribes dare to trespass on the grounds of an unfriendly tribe, for surely warfare would result. But if their relationship with another tribe has been good, they will pay a nominal tribute to its sheikh, who then acts as host to them. The host thus assumes full protection for his guests—even to keeping them safe from enemy raiders.

The early moves of the Bedouins are slow and leisurely and pleasant. There is no hurry. There are many months ahead before the hot sun will again dry up the grasses and force retreat to the well areas.

The moving of the Bedouin camp and its herds to another pasture ground is called *rahla*. The time and the place of the *rahla* is discussed by a council (*mejlis*) of the elders of the tribe with the sheikh. At dawn on the appointed day all eyes are turned to the sheikh's tent. If, for some reason, the sheikh's tent is still standing an hour past sunrise, the people know they may as well send the animals to pasture. "There will be no *rahla* today." But if his women have started to take down the great tent, all know that this day is the *rahla*. The other housewives hurry to take out the pegs of their tents. One neighbor sees another move and hastily sets to work. Soon the whole encampment is busy preparing for the move.

The tent is always the responsibility of the women. As they make the tent a home, they also ready it for moving. After the tent pegs are pulled up, the tent cloth is rolled up, and the tent poles are gathered together and bound. The wife places all her household goods—pots and pans, flour, rice and coffee—in sacks that she wove long ago. As the women are packing the men sit till the last moment warming themselves over small fires, perhaps drinking coffee. The camels that will carry the loads are led in and placed among the packed goods. Then the herdsmen help the women load the supplies upon the camel. All is girded under the camel's belly with a simple cord.

When the baggage is loaded the women climb into their camel litters, which they also made long ago from pomegranate and tamarisk wood, purchased in the towns. The women bind the parts together with thongs of raw leather and cover them with pale yellow gazelle skins. These basket frames or square crates are canopied over with bright colored woolen or cotton material, which gives protection from the eyes of men and the sun. As the women ride along, with their saddlebags containing their possessions hanging down from each side of the litter, they make a colorful sight.

When the tribe moves, the fighting men under the sheikh lead the procession on their riding camels, with the mares and horses attached to their saddles by long leading ropes. Scouts are ahead to report on the suitability of the land for grazing and water. Behind the main body of the men come the women and the camp gear. The herds of camels and sheep follow slowly, grazing as they go. Thus in a long line the Bedouins proceed across the sands. Perhaps they pass stones set together in threes—signs of old nomad potfires—or they see camel dung bleaching in the sun. Perhaps there are little ovals of stones, which mark the graves of long-dead Bedouins. Always there are the desert bushes, looking as if they grew out of hillocks, as the sand has caught in piles at the roots.

Bedouins pause to water their herd as they cross the desert in search of new grazing land. *Arabian American Oil Company*.

The tribesmen march on, as thousands of tribesmen have marched on before them through the years. After about ten miles the procession stops. This is the new campground —a new home for about ten days. The sheikh forces his camel to kneel, and dismounts, signifying that this is the place. The women—the *hareem*—immediately become busy building their tents, but the men are idle. Perhaps among them someone has gathered some sticks, and kindles a fire in a spot sheltered from the wind. They talk and warm themselves, waiting for their black tents to be ready.

All through the *shita*—the period between the October rains and spring proper, in the middle of February—the

55

Camels travel across the sands.

Arabian American Oil Company.

Bedouins will move in this manner, always searching for new grazing grounds. Autumn is a pleasant time, for the grazing on the new green shoots is good, and the sun is warm. The men are idle, or hunting, or raiding, or protecting the camp from raids. But then the cold winds of December come and the growth of plants stops until spring.

It becomes colder and the moves are harder. Those who can afford them don heavy coats; the poor Bedouin has but a thin summer cloak to protect him against the cold. By January there are frosts and the waterskins freeze. Living is hard, for food and water are now scarce. Perhaps on a move the Bedouin returns to a treasure in the desert: dates buried in the hillocks of the now dry bushes.

The cold of the winter is intense, but at last spring comes, around the middle of February. What a joyous time is spring in the desert! The grasses cover the pale sand; wildflowers dot the countryside with splashes of color. The camels and sheep have plenty to graze on, and there is more than enough milk and *leben*. The camels' humps grow and grow as they become fat, the sheep's tail becomes fat, and even the thin Bedouin seems to be a bit plumper than usual. The calves of the camels are born and after a few weeks they begin to eat the tops of the desert bushes.

All too soon this happy time is over. The desert grasses begin to dry up. The winds grow hot; the sand whirls up in storms. It is the time of the mirage—a kind of optical illusion—when every small depression in the countryside appears to be a lake of water, and bushes and animals are mistaken for distant tents and men. The glare of the sun is intense; the Bedouin must pull his headcloth (*kaffiyah*) across his face to protect himself from the elements. Sometimes the sandstorms are so devastating that the life of the Bedouin is in true danger. If he is on a march between wells, without the protection and security of his tents, there is a chance that he may be lost in the yellowish darkness that is the sandstorm. First in such a storm a small black cloud is seen in the distance. The cloud quickly grows and grows until it covers the horizon and swirls up into the sky. Sometimes lightning flashes. The sand is driven along by high winds. The knowing Bedouin will hastily halt his camel and make it kneel, tail half turned toward the wind. He crawls under the cover of the animal's flank, pulling his cloak over his head. There is nothing he can do but hope and pray. The Bedouin may lie like that for hours until the storm passes.

At the encampment the fine gritty dust has swirled through the goat-hair tents, getting into the food and the cooking pot, into the faces and clothes of the nomad. The Bedouins accept the sandstorms and burning winds, for these, they say, come from God. Knowing the seasons and what they bring, by May first the Bedouin starts moving closer to his previously selected summer campsite.

The Bedouin lingers as long as he can, for he loathes the hot, barren summer when he will pitch his tent, with his neighbors, near the wells. But he can delay only so long. By the first week in June, when the countryside is filled with the haze of the sandstorms, the nomads have made their new homes by the well areas in their tribal territory.

The wells belong permanently to the tribe, unless, of course, an individual or his ancestors have dug a well— then that well is his alone. If the well belongs to the tribe, the tents are pitched near it, and no other Bedouins are permitted to water their camels there. If an individual owns the well, others can come seeking water, but they must bring presents for the use of the water.

All the wells are marked by the tribal *wasm,* or brand.

A Bedouin waters his camels before the trek across the desert continues. *Arabian American Oil Company.*

Migrations with the Seasons

This *wasm* shows the Bedouin world to whom the well belongs. It is usually found cut in the rocky sides of the well, way down on the inside, or perhaps it is engraved on one of the large stones built around the well mouth. There are both dug wells and natural wells. The dug wells are most useful for watering the animals, for water can be pulled up by ropes and buckets and poured into leather watering basins for the camels and sheep. A natural well seldom has permanent water. The entrances are usually cracks in the rocks, or holes which open up thirty or forty feet below into an open, dry cavern. From there are more passages leading to a series of other caverns in other directions. Some of these contain large natural underground lakes. But the water from these lakes is very difficult to get. A man must go down in the cavern with his waterskin and crawl for many yards on his stomach or on all fours before he can get even one skinful of water. Nevertheless, this water is highly prized, for it is usually very good and clear, unlike much water on the desert.

Perhaps the Bedouins have camped in a valley. Close by is a green grove of fruit-bearing wild fig trees. There to the thicket, every few days, come the flocks and the camels which have been grazing in the nearby mountains. The well spring in the grove flows into a little clay pool over which flutters a cloud of small gray birds. The housewives will milk the goats and sheep when they go to the spring, and they fill their waterskins there. The men will bathe in the pool. Below the pool in the valley is a desert thorn, grown to a great size, under whose limbs the Bedouins of the camp may come to sleep, since the tents are now like ovens. An hour after the sun rises the tent poles

A youth fills his goatskin water bag while his camels fill their stomachs. *Arabian American Oil Company.*

are too hot to touch. It is a hard time. There is not enough milk for the women to make butter or *leben* daily. They will take up their spinning, as the men lie lazily, almost overcome with the close air. As each summer day passes, the heat rises. Man and beast need to drink water more often. The food supply drops. Sometimes the coffee hearths are cold, for the coffee beans are gone. The Bedouins languish; some of the men are sent to a nearby village to fetch coffee or rice.

Just when life in camp is most oppressive comes the danger of raids by rival tribes. Everyone in the Bedouin world knows where the various summer camps are. A surprise raid on the animals may be in the offing, for now the camels are at pasture at a distance of several hours from the camp, being brought to the wells only every second or third day. The men of the camp must be ready for defense of the camp, and the rescue of their herds if enemy tribes carry them off. A saddled camel may be kept constantly ready before the tents, so that if danger comes the Bedouin will have no delay in setting off to assist a besieged shepherd.

These hot days, too, are the time of the tax collectors. The tax gatherers for the state will come with an armed party to make sure that the tribe pays its *zakat*, tax. Like the enemy, the tax gatherers know where each Bedouin sheikh has camped for the summer. The tax amounts to about one-fortieth of what a tribe possesses. It is calculated by how many full-grown camels there are, and how many young or half-grown camels. It will include one sheep —or its value—for every forty sheep, whether large or small. There is no tax paid on riding camels or on camels used for carrying the Bedouin baggage from camp to camp.

The payment of tax gives both obligation and protection. The head of state has the right in event of war to call upon all those who have paid him *zakat* to fight for him. If they do not, he can confiscate all their livestock. But, too, once the *zakat* has been paid, the ruler is bound to defend that tribe from all enemies. He is thus responsible for all the members of the tribe as though they were his own children.

It is unfortunate that at the time when the Bedouin is most destitute, he is prey to his enemies, and liable for his tax.

As the Bedouin suffers it becomes hotter. August, the time known as the "Two Dogs," is the hottest month of the summer. The air is now calm. Everyone is hot and weary. The camels have grown thin; their humps have shrunk. But now the Bedouins know relief must come, for the end of summer is nearing. When a certain star, *Suhail* (known to the West as Canopus), rises in the southern skies, it is the signal that summer is over. So eager are some of the nomads to see this sign of the end of their summer torment that they will form a watch and arise each day at three A.M. to search the skies.

Then, when the star is seen, the news travels quickly.

"*Suhail* has been seen . . . thanks be to Allah."

Summer is truly ending. Thunderstorms come. There is a breeze, and the smell of the first rain on the dry desert is cause for excitement. Rain! The end of summer! The grass will grow again, and there will be plenty! Now appears the small fat-bodied spider, the Daughter of Rain. The scarlet creature has come out of the wet sand. The men bring in samples of green grasses they have found out in the desert. The Bedouin can live again!

fIVe

Bedouin customs

Among many tribes it is a duty for a Bedouin to marry and have children, for the strength of the tribe depends upon its numbers. But indeed it would be a foolish Bedouin who did not marry, for a man would be very lonely in the desert tribes without a tent. It is the wife who makes the tent, fetches wood and water, loads the baggage, makes the bread, and cooks the meals. Although the Bedouin wife is the mainstay of the household, she, unfortunately, is replaceable. Marriage and divorce are very simple matters in the desert, and many men have been known to have more than one wife. However, the choice of a partner must be approved by the members of the tribe. There are many rules as to whom a Bedouin may *not* marry, such as a member of an inferior tribe, or a person of a special relationship to the family. Every girl, when she reaches puberty, belongs for marriage to her first cousin, the son of her father's brother. Unless this cousin renounces his right to marry the girl, she must marry him. The wedding ceremony varies with the tribe. Some tribes have no ceremony as such, but

A young man of marriageable age.

Arabian American Oil Company.

merely kill a camel as a wedding sacrifice, thus providing a good supper for all while the new wife joins her husband's family tent.

The birth of a child often is not cause for any celebration, although the nomads are much more impressed with the birth of a boy than with a girl. One of the mother's special privileges within the family is to name the new child, which she often does with whimsy. One child born during a heavy rain was called *Matar* (Rain). When the baby is little some tribes dictate that a dagger, a piece of steel, or even a needle must be placed in the cot or attached to the clothes of the baby, to ward off the "evil eye."

When the children are young they live in the women's compartment and help with the lighter chores. They go to their father only for an occasional talk. If they are to be punished their mothers spank them with a stick. The younger children will play about the tent and the desert, often times without clothes, their lithe bodies becoming brown in the sun.

The young Bedouin boy can be called a child of nature. His parents allow him great freedom to do as he wills. His training or education on the desert is to be taught the dangers and rigors of nomadic life, and to learn to shoot and hunt. (Only in recent years have the Bedouin children been able to attend village schools.) The young boys, when not helping their parents with a specific task, will spend their time in play. Some of the games are simple, others are quite dangerous, but none are considered idle, for they toughen the boys and sharpen their skills.

In one popular game the boys form two lines. Those in each line hold hands, and from the starting position ad-

A youth learns the tasks, attitudes, and duties of the men.
Arabian American Oil Company.

vance upon the other line, kicking at their opponents. The game ends when one whole side rolls down on the ground, the boys perhaps having been kicked black and blue on the stomachs. Only when the pain becomes too great will one side give up.

A dangerous game is played with slings and pebbles. Two opposing groups are formed and "war" is declared. Slinging the stones, each team tries to hit as many boys on the other team as possible. Although there are always many injuries

—perhaps a damaged eye, a cracked head, or a broken bone —the parents never forbid the game.

Other games involve skill in running, throwing, or marksmanship. The boys learn to shoot, and shoot straight, by the time they are fourteen years old. Undoubtedly by the time they are sixteen they will have taken part in a raid. The older boys have less time for the frivolity of games. They have the responsibility of learning the tasks, the attitudes, and the duties of men, for each one knows that someday he will be the master of a tent. They tend to the mares, bring fuel to the men's quarters, serve guests with water, and squat with the men around the tent fire, learning about the desert world as they listen to the conversation and learn to recite poems and songs.

The young girls help their mothers with the various household tasks. They must learn to cook, to sew, to weave, and to do all the jobs necessary in supervising a desert household. They may learn songs and prayers and poems from their mothers and other female relatives who live in the tent with them, but formal education is most limited. And this is as it must be, for in her early teens a girl will be married, and become responsible for a tent house of her own.

The question of clothing for very little boys and girls is of small importance. As the children grow older they wear the same type of clothes as their parents. These vary from tribe to tribe, and within the tribe there are variations according to the wealth of the Bedouin. The poor Bedouin man wears a thin cotton smock, which is replaced only when it falls off his back. His cloak, *'Abba,* will most likely be threadbare. He will wear a headcloth, *kaffiyah,* which is held in position by the *'Agal,* head cord. The well-to-do Bedouin will wear basically the same clothing, but his cloak will be made of finely woven sheep's or camel's wool, and might be edged with fine gold embroidery with tassels. His smock or shirt, the *Thaub,* reaching to the heels, may have tight-fitting sleeves, but long wide sleeves are more common. In addition, the prosperous Bedouin will wear over his *Thaub* a *zibún,* a superior type of long shirt, open the length of the front, with wide sleeves that are lined and worn folded back. Both *Thaub* and *zibún* are fastened to the body by a leather or woolen belt. The kerchiefs on the headgear vary widely; they can be black and red, or blue-and-red checkered, or

A little girl with her two-month-old goat.
Arabian American Oil Company.

A Bedouin in his headcloth.

Arabian American Oil Company.

even with yellow stripes. Generally only a sheikh wears a silken white kerchief. Most Bedouins prefer to go barefoot; sometimes, however, a sole cut from camel's hide is tied around the heel and toes. Seldom are riding boots worn.

The Bedouin woman wears a long-sleeved dress, or shirt, of colored cotton, over which is worn the black cotton *Thaub.* The women, like the men, wear the *'Abba;* this black woolen cloak is usually worn outside the tent if there are men nearby. The head and face coverings vary widely, according to tribal custom. Some Bedouin women wear a *Burqa,* a black coarse silk mask with slits for the eyes, which hangs down over the mouth and neck and is kept in place by cords. Other women cover only the lower parts of their faces with a thin black veil. In many tribes the women wear no veiling at all. Again, like the men, most women go barefoot. They also enjoy wearing jewelry, bracelets of beads or coral, necklaces, finger rings, and even nose rings. They will save up camel's hair for a long time in order to be able to sell it and buy jewelry on a visit to a town.

Each tribe has its special or favorite towns to which it goes for its necessities. Such visits, called *musá belah,* are looked forward to with joy. After the dry dust of the desert, the green oasis of the town is a delight. The tall palm trees, the walled orchards, the clay towers, the clutter of the *suks* (marketplaces), are a pleasant sight for the Bedouin who has so little diversion on the desert. Here in the town he buys his coffee beans, corn or grain, and his dates. His wife may purchase gold jewelry or a piece of cloth. The Bedouin barters for his goods, or perhaps he has silver, received from the sale of some of his camels. Although the nomads enjoy the excitement of the towns, they are always happy to return once more to their desert homes.

SIX

RAIDS AND WARS

A hundred camel riders surged across the desert; the nomads sat loosely on the saddle pads, grasping their lances. The horses ran alongside, tied to the camels, in readiness for that moment when the enemy was sighted. Marching along to battle, the Bedouins sang their song:

"O Allah! we beg of thee, thou forgiver,
O Lord of the stairs which lead up to the heights!
To let our luck uplift itself
With the first she-camel and the last one too."*

Off for a raid the men went, with high spirits and high hopes for booty. They expected to capture camels and mares, so each might become richer. They also hoped there would be no bloodshed, for the Bedouin loved to display his cunning, his endurance, and his courage, but he disliked the shedding of blood. He was, perhaps, even more excited about the challenge of the raid than about the number of animals he might capture.

Up until World War II raiding was considered an honor-

* Rwala marching song.

73

Raiding parties dreamed of capturing many camels.
Arabian American Oil Company.

able occupation. It was manly and sporting, and showed who were the truly brave and hard men of the tribe. Raiding had been important to the Bedouins for hundreds of years.

The preparations for a raid were time-consuming. The commander announced to his chiefs that a raid was to be undertaken: "Behold! we wish to go on a large raid under the leadership of the All-Highest. Shoe your horse and prepare supplies for yourselves." The leaders answered: "O Allah, may success be our lot! May He grant us luck!" Then they began to hunt for their supplies—the camel bags, flour, water bags, and barley for the horses. The horses were shod and extra horseshoes packed. There was an air of anticipation in the camp. No one but a few men closest to the commander knew what tribe was to be raided, or where. One could not be too cautious! Who knew who would hear of the plans and warn the enemy?

On the appointed day the tribesmen assembled at a prearranged spot. A guide familiar with watering places was there. So was a sorcerer, or seer, to whom, the commander of the raid believed, Allah sent dreams of special meaning. It was a favorable sign if the seer had dreamed of a mare or a she-camel, or that he had kissed a girl, or eaten dates. All these dreams meant that the raiding party would capture many camels. If he had eaten meat in his dream, it meant that tents would be captured. If he dreamed that he was standing on a high hill, it meant that the commander would score a great victory over the enemy. But if, in his dreams, he saw a man with his front teeth knocked out, or if the dreamer fell down a well, the raid was ill-fated. And it was an especially evil omen if he put on a red jacket in his dreams, for then the commander would surely see his blood flow in battle.

Horses and raiders of the past.   *New York Public Library.*

After all the men had assembled, the leader told them their destination. He also had decided how the spoils would be divided if the raid was successful. Then off they went, with two or three scouts riding ahead of the other men to scan the countryside as far distant as the next night's stopping place.

Of course, if the tribesmen encountered enemy riders along the way, there was a battle. The outcome determined whether they would give up the whole idea of the raid on the selected enemy, and return to camp, or would go on with the scheme. If there was no trouble, however, and a good report from the scouting party, the raiders convened at the night's resting spot. The horses were watered and fed, the camels were set out to graze, and the Bedouins prepared supper for themselves, most often in groups of five or six men each. Their spirits were still high, for they hoped they would soon successfully raid their enemy, and return to their kin.

After midnight the commander again sent out scouts. The tribesmen arose early and resumed their march.

The Bedouins rode on and on; sometimes the object of a raid was over a hundred miles away from their home camp.

Then the enemy camp was finally sighted. Spies learned the strength and placement of the enemy, and—most important—the location of the pastures that held the booty. The leader checked his own ranks. The tired or slow animals were loaded with the baggage of the raiders and sent back to the site of the previous night's encampment, to await news of success or failure. The strong, fast animals were kept to be used by the raiders. The camels were mounted, each by two men. Each horse was ridden by a tribesman, carrying arms if he had them and, hopefully, a spear. The leader rode on horseback at the head of the group. Cautiously they drew nearer and nearer to the enemy. Then they hid so as not to be observed; those on camelback waited quietly. The men on horseback prepared themselves for battle.

Even in war there were rules. There was an "honorable" time for attack. It could be at sunrise when the left forelegs of the resting camels were being unfettered; it could be when the herds started off for pasture, or in the evening when the herds were scattered at pasture; or the time could be after they had been brought back to the camp, but were still unfettered. It was considered fair to attack at any of those times, for then the enemy could defend himself and his animals. But it was thought to be most dishonorable to attack after midnight. Then it would be dark; the men and the dogs would be asleep; if they were surprised, the enemy Bedouins could not defend themselves.

The time for attack came! The leader motioned for the horsemen to advance, ordering, "Gain success, O ye looters!" The horsemen shouted: "O Allah, by Allah Himself!" and charged into the herds, driving the enemy camels with their spears, each man beseeching the others to see what he had captured.

Quickly the captured camels were rounded up and taken by the horsemen to the leader, who had been waiting with the camel riders. Then the horsemen split up. One group armed with spears drove the captured camels back to the last camping site; the other group, armed with rifles, hid and waited with the leader for the enemy counterattack, for there was bound to be an attempt by the enemy to rescue his herd.

Raids and Wars

The enemy leader had spies to report to him. An alarm was sounded in the enemy camp, and there was a din of confusion as the men rushed for their arms and camels. If they found out that the attackers were too strong, they sent messengers to other camps asking for help in pursuing the attackers. A battle would probably follow, but it would not be a battle to the death, for the Bedouins were not so foolish as to needlessly throw away their lives. If the tribe that had been robbed could not make a successful counter-attack, it would scatter. Then the original attackers would move in with their camel riders to the enemy camp. They took what they wanted from the tents, and then took the tents, too, rolling them up and loading them on the camels. The women and children, of course, were left unharmed.

The raiders were successful; they started their victorious ride home, driving their booty, singing about battles and raids. When at last they were near their own camp again they broke into songs of booty and glory. In camp, each man headed for his own tent with his newly captured animals. The women and girls greeted the returning heroes.

Within three days after their return the leader offered the customary sacrifice of a she-camel. As he killed the camel he said, "O Allah, this is our custom. This belongs to the face of Allah and to the face of our ancestor!" As the animal was killed the blood was caught in an iron sheet which was generally used for baking bread. The captured camels' humps and necks were smeared with the blood. This act insured the winning of new booty in the future.

The poor tribe that had lost its camels to a raider would make every effort to pursue the attacker and recapture its camels. One such pursuing party was out three nights.

There were only a few men left in the camp, who worried and drank coffee. The women spent the days straining their eyes to catch sight of the returning tribesmen. They finally called out with cheers when they saw the party returning, but their gaiety soon dispelled, for the men who came riding in were leading nothing home with them. The nomads who had been left in camp shrugged as they saw the party approaching empty-handed, and went to the *mejlis* (the council of elders) to wait for the news. Each returning Bedouin went directly to his own tent, and his wife came forth as her husband made his camel kneel. The housewife spoke not a word, but unsaddled the animal. The nomad did not

A successful raid might have been celebrated like this.
Arabian American Oil Company.

speak then either, for he first had to report to the council.

When the members had assembled, one spoke. "Peace be with you," he said, as he began to tell of the fate of the rescue party. With sadness he related how, on the second day out, they came to a place where the wind had blown away all trace of the attackers' prints. "So Allah willed it," he said, sighing. Because the prints were gone, the party returned. They had traveled over two hundred miles and returned without their stolen cattle. But the Bedouins consoled themselves. "By and by we shall know which tribesmen robbed our camels; then will we *ghrazzy* (foray) upon them and God willing, take as many of them again."

Even in the heat of the year, when the Bedouins were most weary, they would go out together on a raid. Perhaps they took with them only a handful of *meersey* for nourishment. They would be many days together attempting to raid, uncertain of capturing booty, or of even returning alive to their camps, sure only of the fatigue that would finally overtake them. Yet the raiding continued for centuries, for that was the Bedouin way of life before governments could begin to control the nomads.

Wars between tribes were different from raids, for they were not conceived in stealth and secrecy. There were regular rules which had to be openly observed. First of all there had to be a proper and respectable declaration of war. The tribe that wanted war informed the tribe it wished to fight that *niga,* the "warning of war," had been sent to them. They might also send along the news that a certain celebrated warrior would be pitted against the other tribe. When the sheikh of the tribe which had received the *niga* called together his council and announced the declaration

The coffee ceremony has also been a part of war.

Arabian American Oil Company.

of war, he also spoke of the famous warrior, and filled a cup of coffee. Holding the cup, he called out that it stood for the great warrior of the challenging tribe. "Who of you will drink it? Who will take him on in single combat?" the sheikh asked. One of the young men would rise and say, "I am ready." The cup of coffee was passed to him and he drank it. As the names of other warriors were called out, other youths of the challenged tribe pledged to fight them. Then, when the war was actually about to begin, the individual combats were engaged in first, while the soon-to-be-warring tribesmen looked on.

The leaders of the tribes had held councils for weeks and perhaps months before the actual warfare began. They had planned the strategy and the methods of the attacks. The main object of the war between tribes was to seize as many of the enemy's camels as possible, then to wound as much as possible the young men of the opposing tribe. (The old and the very young were left back at the camp to guard the tents and camels there.) Summer was the best time for warring, for then the tribes were at their camps near the wells, and the animals were out at pasture some distance away.

As they went into battle the Bedouins gave forth with their war cries, of which each tribe had at least one of its own. With shouts and yelling, the wild horsemen charged into their enemy. The leader encouraged his men with his bravery. He hesitated not but rushed in. "I fill even heroes with fear," he called. Many of the young fighters raised the hem of their cloak before their eyes with their left hand, and with a sabre or dagger in the right hand threw themselves on the enemy, shouting, "Away! Tremble, O faithless people! Ye shall not escape." If a warrior saw certain death before him, he could ask for pardon, which he would receive from his enemy, who took his arms, most of his cloth-

83

ing, and his mare or camel, but not his life. When both sides of the warring tribes decided that the fighting had gone on long enough, a sheikh would ask for peace, which was seldom refused. Such an offer of peace might have been as follows: "Our people attack yours, and your people ours. There is no profit in it either for you or for us. Why this constant injury? From today we are your friends. All that has happened we have already buried. Decide as you like and then let us know. Greetings!"

The answer would likely have been: "We inform you of the great joy we feel because you desire our friendship. Farewell." The tribal chiefs met and the peace treaty was made. The chiefs grasped each other's right hand and said, "I give thee Allah and the peace of Allah." Thus the war between tribes was over.

In war it is almost impossible to recognize an individual, for the Bedouin goes into battle with his headcloth covering all of his face except the eyes. He hopes that if there should be hand-to-hand fighting and he kills his foe he will not be recognized. If he should be identified, however, as having deliberately engaged and killed another, he must fear for the rest of his life that the dead man's relatives might some day try to take vengeance. The old law, "an eye for an eye and a tooth for a tooth," is understood by all Bedouins. If a man is killed intentionally, the slayer's own life is forfeit. If a man wounds another, he in turn may be wounded. Blood money—payment for death and injury—is possible, but in the desert, justice is more often done by punishing the evildoer with the crime he has committed. The decision depends upon the wishes of the relatives of the person killed or injured. If a murdered man's relatives say they will accept money, the matter can be settled thus; if not, the slayer must lose his own life. And this retribution must be carried out with exactly the same deed as was dealt the dead man. Thus if a man was shot in the head, his slayer must be shot in the head. If only a wound was made, exactly the same type of wound has to be made on the criminal.

The story is told of a tribal woman, living in the desert, who had three sons. The two oldest brothers quarreled one day in the marketplace. The older, in a fit of rage, shot his brother through the heart. This son died. The murderer was arrested. The sheikh of the tribe asked the mother what type of punishment she wished to befall the guilty son. She demanded that her youngest son shoot his elder brother. The sheikh was horrified and pleaded with the mother, but she was determined. Thus the third son, who was good friends with his brother, was ordered to shoot him. He could not do so; he fainted, and the sheikh's men were obliged to carry out the mother's wishes. It was a sorry occasion, but the desert-dwellers approved of the decision.

Although the law, "an eye for an eye and a tooth for a tooth" is understood throughout all of the desert lands, its interpretation and enforcement will vary with the locality and the tribe. In another case, a Bedouin struck his wife with a pestle from a big mortar, breaking her head. She later died. However, the verdict was that her husband had struck her only in anger—he had not meant to kill her, and therefore her kin were not entitled to payment of any kind.

In sha' Allah! It is the will of Allah that it should be so, say the Bedouins.

animals
of the desert

Camels are the Bedouins' most cherished possessions. They can barter the camels for goods or sell them for money to the camel buyers, so the strength and number of the herd determines the wealth of the tribe. The camel is also prized for its milk, which for some Bedouins is the only source of food during the devastating, hot, dry summers.

Since the camels are so important for the Bedouin livelihood they arouse much jealousy among the tribes, and this, in turn, often leads to raids upon enemy tribes. So many were the raids in the desert that an unwritten code of camel laws came into existence. Each camel is marked with the tribal *wasm,* or brand, so all know to which tribe each camel legally belongs. When it is captured, stolen, or lost, each tribe knows what it must do about the camel, according to the laws. For example, if a camel is captured in a raid, it may be kept, but it may also be recaptured by the original owner.

Each herd of camels has its own herdsman who takes the camels out to graze. As he brings them back to the camp,

A Bedouin's most cherished possessions.

Arabian American Oil Company.

riding on his camel, he sings a short, drawling song of his own making. The camels become used to this song, and as they join the other herds in the camp they keep together while the herdsman sings. He halts his camel at his tent, and keeps on singing until all the herd has come in. Then he dismounts and makes each animal kneel down in the place allotted to it. Sometimes during the day, however, a camel may stray from the herd. Then comes the evening, and the herd has been shepherded off to camp. The lost camel will moan for the herd that is no longer in sight. Being accustomed to following the lead camel, the lost one now rambles aimlessly. It may wander off to a different tribe, but happy is the time when the camel eventually returns to its own camp and hears the familiar voice of its own herdsman.

Many of the Bedouin tribes have members who have uncanny skills at tracking—looking at the traces of man or beast in the sand, and being able to tell exactly the type of person or animal that has passed there. Some trackers have skill so great that they can state whether the person was married or single and how tall he was, or whether a camel was white, brown, or black, male or female, in calf or not.

Tracking is considered something akin to an extra sense. The trackers do not depend on a knowledge of the ground or the stars, as do ordinary guides, but on some unusual insight given to them.

Bedouin camels thrive during spring pasturing. There is plenty for them to eat then, and enough water. They are strong and they put on flesh and fat in the humps. They almost frolic out to pasture and bounce into the camp at evening. During the nights, in front of the tents, they chew their cuds until dawn. Sometimes they even arise to go grazing near the tent in the moonlight. They do not wander far, however.

The camel calves are born in the spring. The calf's first voice sounds like that of the sheep's complaint, *bah-bah*. Its fleece is soft as silk, and it leaps about on long legs. The day after its birth the little camel will follow its mother to the field, and in a few weeks will nibble at the bushes. With each month the value of the camel calf rises.

The camel, when it is older, will either be sold, kept for milk, or used as a riding camel on the long marches or in raids. The pure white camel is prized above all, but it cannot be used on a dangerous trip, such as a raid, because its color makes it conspicuous to the enemy at a great distance. Nevertheless it is held in high esteem. Camels can also be light brown, yellowish, ash-gray, or black. They eat bushes of the desert and, in season, wildflowers and grasses of every description. The camel also likes dates which are given to it with milk when it is being prepared for hard work.

Some Bedouin tribes own only one or two camels, for carrying their supplies. These tribes have had their wealth of camels raided away from them in the past, and they have no heart for warfare, so now they are content to own only flocks of sheep and a few goats.

The sheep of the nomads are not all of one kind. Some are great sheep which have gaunt, bony frames and rough and hairy fleece; others are the small sheep, with coarse, short wool. The Bedouins prefer sheep, but most tribes also try to keep a certain number of goats, mainly because of their milk and hair. The goat's hair is superior to the sheep's wool for making certain parts of the black tent, and the milk is necessary for the sustenance of the nomads. Some of the tribes are able to sell the wool from both animals to wandering traders, but most often the women save all the wool they can, and spin yarn from it for tent weaving. There is no special time for the shearing of the sheep's fleece and the clipping of the goat's wool and hair. When the housewife sees an animal with a long coat, she will have it

A desert oasis. *Arabian American Oil Company.*

seized by a herdsman. Then with a blade she will cut off what she can and pluck it out. After the housewife has separated the wool by color, it is put together for spinning. From the sheep's milk she makes the *leben,* by rocking the milk in a goatskin for several hours.

When the sun has been up for half an hour the shepherd will call to his flock of sheep and goats. After they have nursed their young he takes them out into the desert for grazing. The lambs are taken from the tent under a youth's supervision, to learn to graze only a short distance from the campsite. They are brought in at sunset and each is tied by a loop attached to a long goat-hair rope within the tent.

Animals of the Desert

About an hour after sunset, the shepherd brings in his flock of sheep and goats. In many tribes each sheep and goat is given a name. Amazingly, an animal will come to the call of its name, and the shepherd can identify each beast. After nursing, the lambs are taken back and tied again inside the tent, and the sheep crouch down outside.

As it grows dark, the tent watchdogs start prowling around the tents. It is their job to guard the camels, sheep, and goats from wolves and strangers. They are fierce, shaggy animals who bay and bark and keep the shepherd alert to any danger. The biggest danger is from the wolves, which will spring into a camp and cart off a lamb or kid in their jaws, especially on moonless nights. The hounds might well bark on until midnight, and the next day will seem bleary-eyed and weary. They are never allowed inside the tents, as they are considered unclean, but will sleep outside the women's compartments. The dogs are fed with leftovers from the meals, if there are any.

Camp watchdogs.   *New York Public Library.*

Many tribes keep another type of dog—the greyhound, or *saluqi*. The *saluqi* is a small, swift-footed animal trained for hunting hare and gazelle. Unlike the watchdogs, the *saluqi* is considered clean, and is treated gently and with patience. It is allowed to enter the tent at all times, and often lies about on rugs or mats.

In hunting, several Bedouin youth may go out on foot, accompanied by two or three *saluqis*. When a hare is startled up, the dogs will race after it and either break its back or run it to the ground. When gazelles are sought, the huntsmen ride camels, and sometimes the dogs and camels will gallop for miles before the gazelle is caught, and then killed, by the huntsmen.

Another animal that is given preferential treatment by the Bedouin is his mare. She is practically a member of the tent family. She is valued because she will give her owner colts which can be sold. Horses are sold as soon as a buyer can be found, but the family mare always remains, and is loved and cared for as if she were a daughter of the house. A mare may enter the tent for shelter during a cold night, or walk into the women's compartments to escape the burning heat of a midday summer sun. And water will be given to a mare even if it means depriving the tent household of water for coffee.

The mare has been shackled during the night with iron links which, in the morning, are opened with a key to release her. She wanders about the tent in search of grass, and then seeks pasturage with the other horses of the camp. At high noon the mares may return to the tent for water. They will go back to the pasture then, or perhaps, if it is hot, merely stand by the master's tent. When the sun begins to set they head home voluntarily or are fetched. Before she is tethered for the night, the mare may go into the house-holder's booth and nuzzle up to the men sitting around the coffee hearth.

There is really no set time for the mare to be watered. When she is thirsty she will come into the women's quarters and whinny. The women know what the mare wants, so they fetch her water. Like the camels and the sheep of the desert, the mare drinks little in the winter months and early spring. She may be given an occasional bowl of camel's milk. But during the early summer months she will need to drink once a day, and at the height of the hot, dry summer she must be watered three times a day. The mares are seldom given grain, except to get them in condition for a raid or a war, or when the summer grazing is so poor the mares need feed to stay alive.

No one would think of being harsh or cruel to the mare, for Mohammed had written in the Koran that every man should love his horse. He said, "He who loves his mare and treats her kindly shall have God's bounty, and he who ill treats his mare shall be cursed of God."

Even in her old age the mare is treated gently. Gradually she is ridden less and less, until she is given no work at all. She is never killed because of her uselessness; in the end she just lies down and quietly dies.

Mares have a relatively long life, and at the age of twenty many of them are still doing good work for their Bedouin masters. They are rarely sold, unlike the other horses, which are not held in such esteem. Some Bedouins, however, have sold their mares, receiving as much as ten camels for a yearling mare, and from fifteen to thirty thoroughbred riding camels for a three-, four-, or five-year-old mare.

Among the Bedouins there are very few mares that are owned by one man only. (If a mare is owned by one man, generally he is rich.) Two tribesmen may jointly own a mare and, of course, her offspring when she has them. Sometimes half a dozen men may have a share in a mare, and sometimes these nomads may live great distances from one another. In such a case a sale of the mare becomes a very difficult matter, for no one can sell a mare without the permission of all the owners.

The mares are not used for long trips, which are made on camels, but are ridden when paying a visit to a neighbor-

An Arab and his steed.   *New York Public Library.*

ing camp, repelling an enemy attack, or attacking an enemy's herds. The Bedouins place little value on a mare that can run swiftly over a short distance; a good mare must have staying power, for in raids and counter-raids, it is necessary to have an animal with the stamina to keep her rider safe.

In riding, the average Bedouin never uses a saddle or stirrups, but rides bareback, controlling and guiding the animal with halters. It is necessary in the desert to have the horses and mares shod with crude horseshoes to prevent stones and pebbles from hurting the animal's feet. These shoes are replaced only when the old ones fall off. Often a tribe will have a blacksmith traveling with them as they march from encampment to encampment.

If a foal is born during the day, the Bedouins consider the event a lucky one, and claim that the young animal will turn out well. After it is born the foal has the tips of its ears sewn together, so that they will stand up straight when the foal is older. The stitches are taken out after a week. The foal's legs are well rubbed and pulled straight. This, the Bedouins hope, will insure that the horse will have straight legs forever. By the time the foal is three years old it is ridden, and little by little is taken out on marches. By the time it is four years old it can be ridden anywhere.

Aside from the Bedouins' own animals, the desert abounds with wildlife. In its desolate cliffs are nests of sticks which belong to the falcons, the buzzards, and the owls, who screech in the still night. In the dry soil live the rats and lizards and hares. The desert hare is a delicacy for the Bedouins, who much too often exist on a milk diet. A simple fire of sticks and a knife to cut the throat of the hare are all that is needed to prepare the meal; the hare is roasted whole in the skin. The nomads consider its meat tender and tasty. A hare can be felled by a poor Bedouin with the cast of a stone.

If a Bedouin is well-to-do, he may possess a falcon for hawking. Many years ago falconry was considered by the Arabs to be a sport only for sheikhs. Now the sport is more common. If a number of men are on a march, perhaps some of them will carry their falcons with them on the journey. While the camels pasture, they let the hawks capture as many hares as they can scare up. In the encampment the falcons will be tied by one foot to their perches, which are set up in the sand. A good falconer will supply hares almost every day for the family supper. The need for fresh meat will persuade a Bedouin to hawk also for gazelle; the bird attacks the gazelle continuously until the gazelle lies down and the hunter comes up and seizes it. Falcons, which must be trained to hunt, most frequently pursue the *hubara*, or bustard, a large bird that is found in the inland desert.

Another edible animal found on the desert is the *thob*, a large lizard. When grown it is nearly a yard long, including its tail. In the winter it burrows under the hard gravel soil. The hunter of *thob* finds the lizard's hole in the desert, puts a long reed with an iron hook down the hole, and draws the animal out. The Bedouin then cuts its throat and flings the carcass whole upon the coals. When the *thob* is baked, the nomads consider its meat delicious.

Some tribes will eat hedgehogs and porcupines. Rarely is the wolf sought after for food, but if by chance it is shot the nomads will eat it, saying it is good "for the aches in the shins." The fox is also eaten by some tribes, as is the hyena.

A Bedouin falconer protects his hand and arm with a heavy leather sleeve. *Arabian American Oil Company.*

Wild animals of the nomad country include the panther, the wildcat, and the badger. The ibex, with its long powerful horns, lives in the mountains and descends often to the plains where it can be captured by the greyhounds. The antelope is also hunted in the pits of the sandy desert. Its flesh is tasty, and the skin is used for making water bags or coverings. Of the smaller animals there are the marmots and the jerboa, a small white rat that lies underground during the daylight and never drinks. The mouse is found everywhere. It even penetrates into tents and carries away food.

There are many types of lizard in the desert beside the *thob,* and snakes, the cobra among them, are also to be found.

In addition to the wild falcon, many other birds are found in the areas where the Bedouins make their tent homes. There are eagles from which not even the falcon is safe. The vulture is shot and eaten, for its flesh is considered healthful. There are storks, ravens, swallows, partridges, and turtledoves.

Perhaps the most striking of any of the wildlife are the locusts. From near the soil the locusts swarm to a great height, then descend from the skies as thick as rain. As they fall they are scooped up by the women and children, put on twigs, and roasted over the coals. As the Bedouins pluck them off the sticks they break away the heads, and tell each other how tasty are the roasted bodies that remain!

So, though the desert life is hard for the nomad, he is helped in his survival by many of the wild creatures which inhabit his land.

Falcons are trained to hunt hares, bustards, and gazelles.

Arabian American Oil Company.

bedouin culture and religion

The Bedouins are a truly proud and independent people. Living amid hardship, they have developed a resistance to adversity, and at the same time a resignation to the inevitable. They accept life as it is. The Bedouin is an honorable man, yet within his code of conduct he will engage in activities, such as raiding another tribe's cattle, that seem dishonorable to other peoples. His principles of living often appear to contradict one another.

The Bedouin has a strong feeling of pride; therefore, insults or slights are considered to be of a very serious nature. But it is this pride and sense of family honor that make the Bedouin so hospitable and so concerned for his fellow men. The Bedouin places grave importance on his responsibility to protect his tent neighbor and any traveler to whom he has guaranteed safe conduct. He also has a duty to offer more than generous hospitality. It is not unusual for a Bedouin to prepare his very last food supplies for strangers who are guests, knowing that he and his family will be reduced to drinking *meersey,* dried milk and water, the next

Hospitality in the desert.   *Arabian American Oil Company.*

day. He quietly insists on giving thus, for praise of his generosity and hospitality increases his honor. His women-folk, too, maintain the family honor, even in the absence of the tent master. A wife, seeing a guest outside the tent, will rush out holding a frothing bowl of camel's milk or *leben*, as a sign of welcome.

Aside from a few visits to town, the Bedouin's daily life is simple. The tribesmen generally live together in harmony. If a dispute or a grievance arises between two Bedouins, the matter is immediately soothed over by their fellows with the assurance that each may present his case at the next day's *mejlis*, the council of the elders and the public tribunal. The nomad sheikhs govern wisely and well. The judgment is given without partiality and always without bribes. The sentence is final; generally the loser pays for his crime with heads of his small animals or camels, or he goes into exile.

First and foremost in the Bedouin's mind is his duty toward God. Although many of the nomads may not know the formal prayers as revealed in the Koran, they are Moslems, followers of the prophet Mohammed. They believe in one almighty God, Allah, and they believe that everything, both good and evil, comes from God. "God gave, God has been pleased to take away," is an expression used often by the Moslems. Thus it is that the desert dweller is always resigned to the events that befall him.

Whether in camp or on the march, the Bedouin must pray five times a day. Before dawn he rises to his prayers; if they are not formal he will at least face Mecca, the Holy City, and murmur toward heaven a phrase or two: "Ah Lord my God!" and "Oh that this day may be fortunate; give Thou

Bedouin Culture and Religion

that we see not the evil!" Then there is coffee, and the beginning of the day. Although the next time for prayer is not until noon, often the Bedouin will speak of God in his conversation: *"Allah!"* when expressing wonder; *"Ya Rabbi!"* (Ah, my Lord!) when weary; *"La-ila-il-l'Allah,"* (There is no God but God). Three and a half hours after noon comes the third prayer. The Bedouin who might well have been resting bestirs himself; he goes forth and falls on his knees, claps his palms upon the sand before him, and rubs them, then draws them down from his forehead; thus he washes the two sides of his face. He again murmurs his prayer, then

A Moslem must pray five times a day.

Arabian American Oil Company.

rises, and perhaps walks about the camp, looking for any new smoke from the black tents, indicating that there is a fire ready for coffee making. Again at sunset, and again at one and a half hours after sunset, after the evening meal, the Bedouins pray to Allah.

Even away from camp, in the wilderness of the desert, the Bedouins will pray. Many are the praying places in the open desert, marked by a narrow horseshoe of stones, the "shoe" bent toward Mecca.

One of the duties of a true Moslem was laid down by Mohammed: to fast for thirty days during the month of *Ramadan*. The fasting begins with the sight of the new moon and ends with the sight of the next new moon, and during this time it is forbidden to drink any water or take any food from two hours before sunrise until sunset. Mohammed said, "He who forsakes the fast of *Ramadan* becomes infidel, whom to deprive of wealth and life is lawful."

Ramadan falls in the ninth month of the Moslem year, but because the Moslems have a lunar calendar (based on the moon), the holy month can occur in any season. How hard it is when *Ramadan* falls in the sun-burning days of summer! To abstain from drinking until the sun sets is almost intolerable, and for the herding men out in the desert, the heat is nearly impossible. With empty stomachs the nomads watch the sunlight as it fades, knowing that when it is gone, they will pray and then have their first night meal. Perhaps even past midnight they will arise from sleep and seek the nourishment of a few dates, or refresh themselves with some *meersey*.

During the month of fasting, the men pray together. They will stand out from the tents at the prayer hours, make ranks, and say the formal prayer, bowing their foreheads and falling upon their knees. *Ramadan* is the only time that the women may be seen praying, kneeling with folded arms before their tents. At other times they say their prayers in the privacy of their tents.

At last the fasting is over! Now is held the joyous festival, the *'Id al-Ramadan,* which officially lasts for three days, though it may be carried on for seven. It is a time of rejoicing and feasting. There may be horse races and camel races, and if there is any spare ammunition in the camp there will be shooting matches. The unmarried and young girls will do their tribal dances within the tent. The elder women will sing as the younger ones dance. It is truly a happy time.

Most of the Bedouins find it difficult to think of an after-

Many are the praying places in the open desert.
Arabian American Oil Company.

life; they pray and fast because those are the duties of their religion. They look for blessings in their present life. When death comes, they bury their dead on the same day as the death occurred, if possible. They dig out a shallow grave in the dry desert, and place the feet of the dead one toward Mecca. On top of the grave they may place a few stones to mark the spot. Although the Bedouins may not concern themselves with the future of the deceased person, often they will honor him, year by year, with a sacrifice. Each householder who pays such homage, to his father or his grandfather, must slay his own sacrifice. Perhaps a young camel is to be offered. The Bedouin will take a knife, tuck up his sleeves, and slit the throat of the captured animal. Soon the camel will be in the pots over the fire, and many will satisfy their hunger at such a feast.

Animals are sometimes sacrificed also as a thank offering when a boy is born. Then the father might slay a young sheep. Sometimes if a camel is ill a goat is sacrificed; or a herdsman who is sick may make a supper of a goat for his friends. The Bedouin thinks the sacrificed sheep or goat takes his own or his camel's place; thus a life for a life.

The Bedouins are not always solemn, however. Many are the merry times they have sitting around the coffee hearth listening to a wandering poet or storyteller. How the laughter rings out then! The Bedouins love to hear, recite, and compose poems.

A poem is rarely written down. Most often the poet's friends learn it by heart, and others learn from them. Practically every Bedouin knows parts of several poems. The Bedouins have been noted for their eloquence of language; some scholars consider that they speak the purest of Arabic.

Bedouin Culture and Religion

This love and skill of language is evident in their poems and storytelling.

The Bedouins believe that a poem should be a work of art. The words used in one must be unusual words, not those used in everyday living. A poet will write and revise every verse most carefully, repeating the poem many times, changing words here and there. He will seek advice from others before declaring his poem finished. And the poet always explains the reason or occasion of the origin of every poem. A poem was written of the lament of a man followed by misfortune, another about the sadness of a father for two sons killed in battle, a third in honor of a prince.

The following poem was composed by a poet who, "Bitten by a Mad Dog and Abandoned by His Kin, Laments to a Friend."

Bedouins are not always solemn.

Arabian American Oil Company.

"This is my lament, the lament of a strange dervish
Parted from the pilgrim throng and left on the camping
  ground.
O Hmûd, take care of me who have been ensnared,
For among my kin is no honest man who would think of
  me.
I am bitten by a mad dog, though they say nothing ails
  me.
Near is the fortieth day appointed for me.
I could walk before the Arabs as if nothing ailed me,
Walk I could, though my entrails were filled with unrest.
What should it mean, O daring one! that my kin shun
  me?
Like a dog, driving me away; ah! They cannot be my kin.
My time is drawing to its end, O hero, and the symptoms
  appear;
In a day or two I shall no more enjoy life."

In this poem the composer was describing a catastrophe
that had befallen him. In truth he had been bitten by a mad
dog, and his relatives had, according to custom, dragged
him to a water hole, and given him enough salt, flour, and
dried dates to last him forty days. (At the end of forty days,
the symptoms of rabies would appear.) They cautioned
him that if he should leave that spot and come near them
before the forty days had passed, they would kill him. Thus
the poet had to stay in the desert by himself. His good
friend, Hmûd, was away on a raid, but when he returned
he went straight to the poet, although only thirty-eight days
had passed since the dog bite. This poem was written for
the faithful Hmûd.

Another poet, noted for his hospitality, composed a poem
which began:

"O Klejib, light the fire, O Klejib, light it!
To light it is thy duty; the fuel will be brought.
To prepare cardamom and coffee beans is my duty,
Thine to have the tarnished pots ready. . . ."

A popular poem about a young girl anxious to appeal to a certain young man goes:

"By Allah, I shall cast thee aside, old dress, and put on a
    new one.
But which is the new and which the old?
If I see a noble youth, my judgment is gone. . . ."

Thus poems are written and recited for many occasions. The verses that pertain to subjects of universal interest are recited over and over again and become widely known.

Many poems or stories are recited to music. The Bedouin singer plays a musical instrument called the *rabab*. It is made of a box frame. A kidskin is stretched over the hollow box. A stick is put through the box, to form the neck of the instrument, and in the stick is pierced a spot for a peg. The string is taken from a mare's tail and a bent twig, the bridge, holds it taut. Playing the instrument, the minstrel sings his songs or tales. The herdsmen who have been out in the desert all day are often the most robust of singers before their audience in the tent.

Stories and legends are also common in the Bedouin camps. The Bedouins love to hear the literature of their people, as eloquently orated. They will listen enrapt to anything, from stories of daring deeds to fables of animals. All of these are entertaining, and many have a moral which should be heeded. One such is the following, told in the desert:

"Once there was a Lion in the forest, and he decided to go hunting with some companions. He called the Wolf and the

Fox to him, and hunt they did. They were very successful. They killed a buffalo, a gazelle, and a hare. Time came for dinner, and the Lion stood up in lordliness and asked his friends how the meat should be divided. The Wolf announced that it was a simple matter to decide. His Majesty, the Lion, would take the buffalo, the Wolf would take the gazelle, and the littlest, the Fox, would take the hare.

"With that statement the Lion roared, and gave the Wolf so violent a blow that his head was torn off and rolled along the ground to the brook. 'Aha,' said the Lion, 'that for your opinion, you rogue.'

"Then he turned to the Fox and noted that all considered the Fox most clever. He asked the Fox how he would divide the meat. The Fox answered that there was only one fair decision. All three—the buffalo, the gazelle, and the hare— would go to the great king, Lion. The Lion praised the Fox's wisdom, but wondered where he had learned such cleverness.

"The Fox pointed to the Wolf's head on the ground and said, 'Oh monarch of the world, the Wolf's head taught me my wisdom.' With that statement the Fox scampered off into the bushes."

nine

Bedouin Superstitions

The monster of the desert has one eye set in the middle of a humanlike head; it has a long beak like a bird; the arms are like baby chicken wings; the body is as big as a camel's, but in the shape of an ostrich. The creature is female and has one foot like a donkey's foot, another like an ostrich. This is the *Ghul*. She wanders over the dry sands calling the nomads by name, enticing them to come. One Bedouin swore by the life of Allah that he and his tribe had seen the *Ghul* dead upon the ground when they were out on a foray, but he said, "None of them dared touch her."

Other people claim there exists a monstrous creature called the *Salewwa*. The *Salewwa* is like a woman, only she has cloven hooves, like the ass. Many persons say they have seen *Salewwas*. One time on a great *ghazu* (raid), eighty men of the tribe saw her as "they alighted in an evening, but when their bullets might not do her scathe, they took up firebrands to beat the woman-fiend, and they beat on her all that night."

The Bedouins have many superstitions, but the most universally believed is that of the *jinn,* or spirits, that can possess one and can cause strange diseases, especially of the mind. The *jinn* often lurk in Bedouin burial places. On a dark night these spirits of the dead come out of their tombs and converse with one another. If any person of the world should happen to pass close by, the spirits shout after him. Sometimes they even throw stones. Many tribesmen swear that they have heard the tread of the spirits' feet in dance and heard their songs by night.

The *jinn* are often thought to have special lighting places in certain trees and shrubs of the desert. At such a tree a sick person will sacrifice a sheep or a goat for his health. The flesh of the animal is cooked and divided among the friends present; some of the flesh is left hanging on the branches. Then the sick person lies down to sleep, believing that the *jinn* will descend upon him and give back his health, and that he will awaken "whole and sound." Some trees which are recognized as belonging to *jinn* are draped with offerings of old beads, shreds of calico, and pieces of colored material.

Some Bedouins think the *jinn* are divided into tribes, clans, and families like the nomads, and live in high mountains, steep ravines, or old ruins. These *jinn* do not have tents but live in underground dens, rock crevices, and caverns. They raise goats and sheep, but in areas so rocky and stony that the Bedouin goats and sheep could not survive there. They are said to like raw meat, which they get from fallen animals, and fresh blood is their favorite drink. They get the blood every time an animal is killed by the Bedouins.

Just as the *jinn* may easily possess a person, so there are certain people who can drive out the demons. These are the "readers," or "reciters," who have learned by heart to recite spells, made out of words from the Koran. The power of "God's word" is thought to frighten the *jinn* and cause it to leave the possessed person.

The Bedouins also believe that certain women, called *sahharas*, can cast spells over men, and can remove the spells at will. Many think such women have direct connection with evil spirits. One *sahhara* wanted to kill a man for slaying her husband. She gave him a mattress and cushion that she had made. Inside the pillow were certain writings, needles, and colored threads, which supposedly could cast a spell and kill. The man who leaned on the pillow was indeed struck with great pain in his head and eyes, but was finally saved by a spell breaker.

People who are said to have "the evil eye," which is feared by many Bedouin tribes, also can cast spells. Often it is not certain who has an evil eye, but if a man lacks both upper eyeteeth or has blue eyes, then it is possible that he is able to bewitch. All will avoid him.

The person who has been bewitched feels at once very weak; his eyes become dim, and he might faint. If the possessor of the evil eye is known, two or three threads are taken from the hem of his clothing and laid on red-hot coals, and the person afflicted is cleansed of the harm by the smoke from the fire.

Then there are seers among the Bedouins. These are men and women who know and see hidden things, and are able to heal the sick. The seer claims that he has communication with an angel, who tells him the will of Allah. The angel appears in the shape of a rider seated on a white mare, and

113

tells the seer what to say in Allah's name. There is much doubt among the Bedouins about the true position of the seer. If a man has parents or grandparents who have been seers, then it is probable that he too will eventually be accepted, but the self-proclaimed seers are often scoffed at.

The disciples of the seer play an important role in divining the future or healing the sick, for it is their job to carry little drums and other musical instruments when the seer is on a call. When the seer, or sorcerer, wants to summon the angel to him, he tells the disciples to play music.

The desert is a lonely place.

Arabian American Oil Company.

The seer squats with his head bent down. Then the music begins. The seer begins to move. He stands up, stretches out his hands, jumps around, puts his hands, feet, and even his head close to the fire, and claps his hands. The seer may not be able to receive news from the angel. He will be laughed at many times. But if a seer is crossed he may curse a man; that man will then be afraid, and will hasten to make peace with the seer and ask his protection.

Sorcerers can tell if it is going to rain and for how long, and whether a wife will have a boy or a girl baby. Of course, they are important when a raid is being undertaken. There are stories of miraculous recoveries of the ill when a sorcerer has been persuaded to come, as in the case of a woman who was paralyzed. After three days of the music and the attention of the seer, she jumped to her feet and began to dance and was well thereafter.

The activities of the fortuneteller, or soothsayer, are viewed as sheer entertainment by some tribesmen and taken very seriously by others. The fortuneteller has a little bag in which she keeps a number of objects. These objects may include pebbles, broken glass, burnt bricks, and pieces of pottery. Generally they include seashells and date stones. When a soothsayer is to tell a fortune she will take the objects from the bag, shake them in the palm of her hand, and throw them at random on the floor. By the positions in which the objects fall, the fortuneteller can read the future. Men of certain tribes have consulted the soothsayer to help them locate lost camels, or to learn whether a relative will return from a raid or not. These men believe that the fortuneteller can help and guide them, and stories of lost sheep and camels being found, told among the tribes, reinforce their belief in the powers of such women.

In their daily life the Bedouins see around them omens and signs that they must follow. The days have their special meanings, and the moon is carefully observed for its waxing and waning. Clans are considered to have good or bad omens. Certain tribesmen, when they were going out on a raid, would prefer to suffer hunger than take a meal with a clan with a bad omen. Animals, too, are considered carriers of good and bad signs. A fox is carefully watched. If it halts when seeing a group of raiders, and looks at the tribesmen from both the right and the left side, then the party will have great success and win rich booty. If a hyena jumps out suddenly before a raiding party, this, too, means good luck. All the raiding tribesmen will shout with enthusiasm if they see two ravens flying from one side to the other above them, for they know this is a good omen. One raven is bad luck, however. A black dog should be killed at sight, for there is a fiend hidden in him. If the raiders on their march meet a flock of sheep they must stop and let the flock pass by, for if they were to ride through it and scatter the animals, they themselves would be scattered and defeated in their battle with the enemy.

The Bedouins pay great attention to dreams. Many sheikhs have had dream interpreters to guide them, both in peace and in war. It is believed that when a man is asleep his soul moves among the spiritual beings, from whom it can learn of things past, present, and future, that are hidden from man. Many Bedouins beseech Allah to send them dreams.

The Bedouins watch the skies, too, for it is known that stars, by moving, can lead one astray at night. Their rays and the rays of the sun are believed to prevent wounds from healing. A wounded person will be tightly wrapped up to keep these rays away. There is a spirit of fatalism among the Bedouins: what happens is the will of Allah. They are not likely to seek medicine for their wounds or illnesses. They place much more faith in the "readers," with their spells of words from the Koran.

Charms and amulets can be worn, both to ease pain and to cure. Such are the *hijabs,* papers written with Allah's words, texts of the Koran altered to fit the need. They are composed by magical men, and are intended to protect or secure something for the owner. *Hijabs* against bullets often take the magical men a month to write. The paper on which the charm is written must be cut the length of the intended wearer and be entirely covered with writing. It will be preserved in a leather case. Before it is delivered to the purchaser, its effectiveness is tested on an animal. It is tied onto a beast, and if the beast escapes from a shot, the charm is considered to be in good working order. One leader, however, who was protected by such a *hijab,* was killed by his enemies with a silver bullet, for they knew that he possessed the charm against lead.

The superstitions are many. If the nomads observe the magical rules they may be fortunate. They are sure, however, that whatever happens will be the will of Allah.

the bedouins today and tomorrow

The proud, hardy, and independent Bedouins often live today the way their ancestors lived. They tend their animals as did their forefathers; they live in the same type of sturdy black goatskin tents. They are driven by winds, blasted by hot sands, and suffer from thirst and often from lack of food. Their tools and equipment are similar to those of hundreds of years ago. Their search for water is everlasting; their moves for good pasturage follow the same patterns as the migrations of a thousand years ago.

Yet today life is changing for the Bedouins. The sand dunes they roamed are being leveled as roads are built. Leading their livestock along, searching for grazing land, they may find a new man-made oasis—a well drilled as part of a government water and agricultural development project. The countries which have always been the home of the Bedouins are modernizing, hoping to develop their lands to the benefit of all of their peoples, including the Bedouins.

The Bedouin of today may look like his father and live like his father, but will he continue to do so? It is doubtful,

Today's Bedouins migrate past oil wells.
Arabian American Oil Company.

Progress is bringing the nomadic life to an end for many.
Saudi Arabia Public Information Service.

for scientific advances are so great that the Bedouin cannot long remain untouched. Dynamite charges and bulldozers have leveled an old palace overlooking the Red Sea, making way for a desalination plant, which will distill fresh water from the water of the warm, salty sea. Land is being reclaimed, and enriched by organic fertilizer. Steel mills are rising. Ways are being sought to more fully utilize natural gas. The oil industry, already huge in many of these areas, is continuing to expand.

The Bedouins are coming into contact with progress, and some of them are choosing to leave their desert ways for a more secure life. The nomad population began to decrease to a limited extent even a hundred years ago, when some of the desert dwellers sought more permanence by settling in the villages, or by becoming partly nomadic—growing crops in a particular area, moving on when new grazing was needed for their animals, but returning once again to their homes away from the desert.

Today, with wells being drilled and land cultivated, settlements are being built by governments in the hopes of luring the Bedouins away from their harsh lives. Each day more and more Bedouins are being absorbed into settled communities. Some are lured to the oil fields, some to the farms, where full-scale agriculture has been introduced. Health standards have been raised, both in the villages and in the remote areas where the Bedouins live. One day there will be many rural hospitals and fleets of mobile health clinics.

There has been a phenomenal growth of schools in the villages, so that many children who previously roamed the desert and learned only nomadic lore around the tents may receive formal education.

Yet, though the number of true Bedouins is diminishing, thousands and thousands of nomads still move across the sands as did their fathers and grandfathers. For example, Saudi Arabia, which occupies about four fifths of the Arabian peninsula—about the size of the eastern half of the United States—is populated at least half by the Bedouins. It is estimated that in Saudi Arabia there are one hundred Bedouin tribes, with a membership of one thousand people each. If the semi-nomadic peoples were included, the total number of wanderers would be two thirds of the country. There are Bedouins, too, of course, in all other countries of the Arabian peninsula.

Until the beginning of the twentieth century the Bedouins were almost totally responsible to themselves. Each tribe had its own rulers and its own laws; taxes and tributes were paid to others, but the Bedouin was basically responsible to his tribe. Today, governments like that of Saudi Arabia are stable, and are the highest authority for all of their citizens, including the Bedouins. The governments have admiration for the nomads, who have been able to survive the rigors of the desert, who have been able to breed livestock under the most trying of conditions. However, government officials would like to expand the opportunities for the Bedouins. They would like to see large numbers of these wanderers transferred to areas where there are fertile pastures, or good farmland, or other employment. Yet these same officials recognize that the Bedouins have been following a migratory pattern for hundreds and hundreds of years. Proud and independent, they have moved with the seasons. How can they accept settlement and an industrial or agricultural occupation? That is the problem.

Former Bedouins find farming a change for the better.
Saudi Arabia Public Information Service.

For others the old life is still the best.

Arabian American Oil Company.

The number of Bedouins will continue to decrease as each country improves its lands, modernizes its technology, learns and practices new agricultural methods, and increases its industrialization. Yet it is likely that for years to come there will be some of the true Bedouins roaming the deserts, moving their camels and their tents. Proudly they will grind coffee beans with mortar and pestle, offering their hospitality to all who come. For they have a heritage; it will be a long time before all of them will relinquish it.

index

* Indicates illustration

Index

Clothing, 15*, 30, 35, 58, 69-72, 71*, 83-84

Coffee, 9, 11, 25-26*, 29, 29*, 30, 32, 40, 42-48*, 44*, 45*, 46*, 47*, 54, 62-63, 80, 81-83, 82*, 93, 103, 104, 109, 124, 124*

Council, tribal, 22, 26, 27, 53, 80-83, 102

Damascus, 13, 17-18, 19

Divorce, 65

Dogs. *See* Animals, Bedouin.

Falcons. *See* Animals, Bedouin.

Families, 22, 24-30, 67, 100, 102

Fortunetellers, 115

Games, 38, 39, 49, 67-69

Goats. *See* Animals, Bedouin.

Hospitality, 9, 11, 35, 41-42, 100-102, 101*, 108-109, 124

Hunting, 49, 50*, 92, 96-99*, 97*

Islam, 14-18, 31, 102-106, 103*, 105*

Jinn, 112

Jewelry, 30, 72

Jewish influence, 14, 16

Kemmaye. See Truffles.

Koran, 93, 102, 113, 117

Lands, tribal, 22, 23, 28, 52-53

Laws
  camel, 86
  "an eye for an eye," 84-85
  marriage, 65
  war, 78

Leben (yogurt), 30, 32, 35, 58, 62, 90, 102

Legends, 109-110

Mares. *See* Animals, Bedouin.

Marriage, 25, 65, 67

Meals, 32, 36, 39-42, 96, 98, 104

Mecca, 13, 15, 16, 17, 31, 102, 104, 106

Medina, 16-17

Meersey, 81, 100, 104

Mohammed, 14-17, 18, 93, 102, 104

Monsters, 111

Moon worship, 14

Moslem Era, 16-18

Musical instruments, 109, 114-115

Native territory, 11-14, 20-21, 122

Omens, 75, 116

Poems, 69, 106-109

Index